Hex

A Playful Introduction

Ryan B. Hayward

AMS / MAA | ANNELI LAX NEW MATHEMATICAL LIBRARY

VOL **54**

Hex

A Playful Introduction

Ryan B. Hayward

Providence, Rhode Island

2020 *Mathematics Subject Classification.* Primary 00A08, 00A09, 91A43, 91A27.

For additional information and updates on this book, visit
www.ams.org/bookpages/nml-54

Library of Congress Cataloging-in-Publication Data

Names: Hayward, Ryan B., 1958- author.
Title: Hex : a playful introduction / Ryan B. Hayward.
Description: Providence, Rhode Island : American Mathematical Society, 2022. | Series: Anneli Lax new mathematical library, 2578-6407 ; volume 54 | Includes bibliographical references and index.
Identifiers: LCCN 2021049630 | ISBN 9781470464929 (paperback) | 9781470469481 (ebook)
Subjects: LCSH: Game theory. | Hex (Game) | Combinatorial analysis. | AMS: General and overarching topics; collections – General and miscellaneous specific topics – Recreational mathematics. | General and overarching topics; collections – General and miscellaneous specific topics – Popularization of mathematics. | Game theory, economics, finance, and other social and behavioral sciences – Game theory – Games involving graphs.
Classification: LCC QA269 .H388 2022 | DDC 519.3–dc23/eng/20211201
LC record available at https://lccn.loc.gov/2021049630

∞ The paper used in this book is acid-free and falls within the guidelines
established to ensure permanence and durability.
Visit the AMS home page at https://www.ams.org/

10 9 8 7 6 5 4 3 2 1   27 26 25 24 23 22

Do you like to play games?

This book is for you.

In memory

Frédéric Maffray (1960-2018),

graph theorist and friend;

Pouneh Gorji (1993-2020) and Arash Pourzarabi (1994-2020),

international scholars;

Audrey Jean Hayward (née Banerd) (1934-2021),

quirky, funny, thoughtful, ever-curious, generous, loving.

contents

acknowledgments

I first saw Hex in 1980 at Queen's University in Kingston, at a math colloquium after-party hosted by my graph theory prof David Gregory. Later in Paris, my McGill University Ph.D. supervisor Vašek Chvátal introduced me to Claude Berge while they were editing a book on graphs. Claude loved Hex and showed me how to play. Thank you David, Vašek and Claude for introducing me to graphs and to Hex.

In 2002 I started a Hex project at the University of Alberta in Edmonton funded by the Natural Sciences and Engineering Research Council of Canada. Many thanks to NSERC and those who helped over the years: Yngvi Björnsson, Michael Johanson, Maryia Kazakevich, Morgan Kan, Nathan Po, Jack van Rijswijck, Philip Henderson, Broderick Arneson, Aja Huang, Jakub Pawlewicz, Brad Thiessen, Henry Brausen, Jesse Huard, Yuri Delanghe, Kenny Young, Noah Weninger, Chao Gao, Nicolas Fabiano, David Pankratz, Jacob Garber, Martin Müller, Emery Smith, Bedir Tapkan, and Jonathan Schaeffer.

In 2019, with the help of Bjarne Toft and Thomas Maarup at the University of Southern Denmark and Hugo Hein in Middelfart, I finished writing *Hex: The Full Story*, a comprehensive history. Stephen Kennedy and John McCleary at the MAA encouraged me to write this companion intro for a general math audience — *Hex: A Playful Introduction* — and gave expert guidance: thank you.

Thanks to Peter Selinger, Eric Demer, Chelsea Chen, Sowmya Challa, Ismail Naderi Beni, and anonymous MAA reviewers for detailed and constructive feedback.

And thank you L, A, E, O, A, and H.

Ryan B. Hayward

preface

Like chess and Go, Hex is a challenging two-player board game. Unlike chess and Go, the rules can be learned in a few seconds.

Hex rules are so simple that some game properties are easy to prove. For example, for any $n \times n$ board, the first player has a winning strategy. Can you show that for chess or Go? Good luck, buddy!

This book it is your introduction to Hex, the math behind the game, and its puzzles. Since 1942 — when Piet Hein invented the game — Hex has intrigued Jens Lindhard, Karen Thorborg, John Nash, David Gale, Claude Shannon, Martin Gardner, and many others.

Now it is your turn. Read on ...

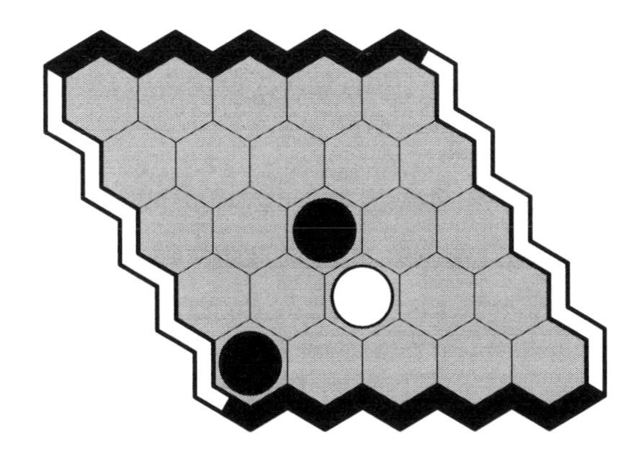

1

this is Hex

Rule-Forty-two. All persons more than a mile high to leave the court.

The King, to Alice in Wonderland.

Here are the rules and some fundamental properties.

1.1 rules

The board is an n by m array of hexagons, usually with n equal to m. Two opposing board edges, or sides, are black. Two opposing board edges are white. Figure 1.1 shows a 5×5 board.

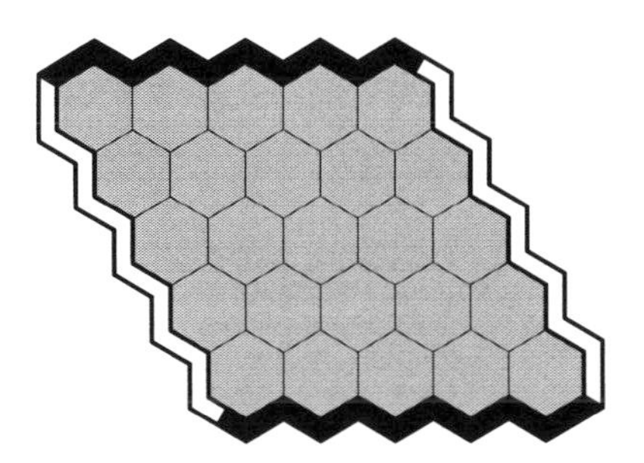

Figure 1.1. A 5×5 Hex board.

There are two players: Black uses black stones (or a black marker), White uses white stones (or a white marker). Players alternate turns: Black usually moves first. On a turn, a player puts a stone on (or marks) an empty cell. A player wins by joining the two edges of their color with a path of their stones (or marks). The path can twist and turn.

And that's it for the original Hex rules! These days, an extra rule is often added to balance the game: the swap rule. To ease understanding, we delay its explanation to Section 1.4.

In case you make your own game set, notice that the maximum number of game moves equals the number of board cells. For example, a 5×5 game set includes the board, at least 13 black stones and at least 12 white stones.

1.2 sample game

Let's look at a sample 5×5 game. Figure 1.2 shows the cell names — rows labelled 1 to 5, columns labelled *a* to *e* — and the game's first several moves. To make it easier to read cell labels, in this book we sometimes draw stones as hexagons rather than circles.

To start, Black takes the center. In game notation, we write this as 1.B[c3], where 1 is the move number, B (Black) is the player who moved, and c3 is the cell where the move was made.

White tries to block Black with 2.W[c4]. Black takes the obtuse corner with 3.B[a5]. White splits Black's stones with 4.W[b4]. Black stops White from reaching the edge with 5.B[a4]. White blocks Black's advance to the top with 6.W[b2].

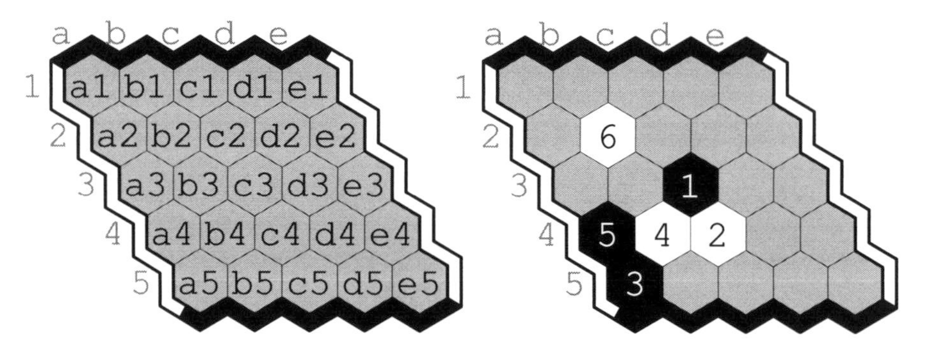

Figure 1.2. Cell names. Opening of sample game.

Figure 1.3 shows the rest of the game. 1.B[c3] is the first move of a simple winning strategy, so Black should have won. Instead, Black blundered away the advantage, because the game ends with 22.W[e5] and White wins.

After move 1, would you have played this game differently? Black could have resigned after move 14: from there, White wins easily. Do you see how? How many errors in play can you find? We will answer these questions in a later chapter.

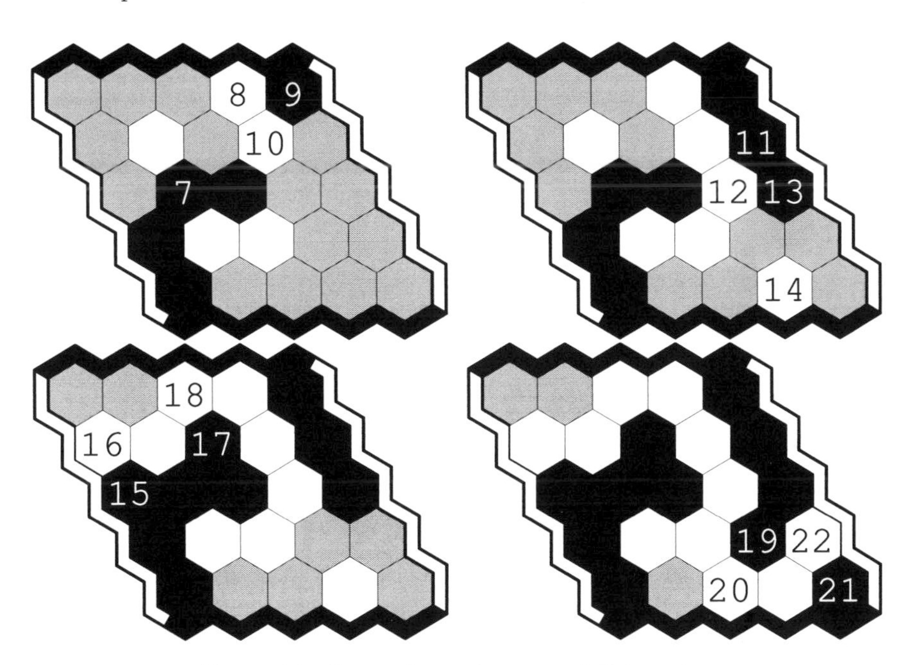

Figure 1.3. Rest of sample game. White wins.

1.3 now it's your turn

Find an opponent and play a game! Draw a simple board as in Figure 1.4: for that board, place stones on dots. Or copy a board from Figure 1.5 or 1.6 or `https://webdocs.cs.ualberta.ca/~hayward/hexbook/hex.html#brd`.

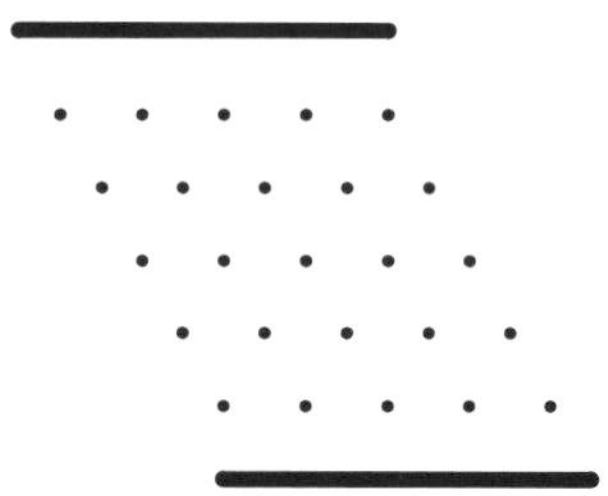

Figure 1.4. Draw a simple Hex board.

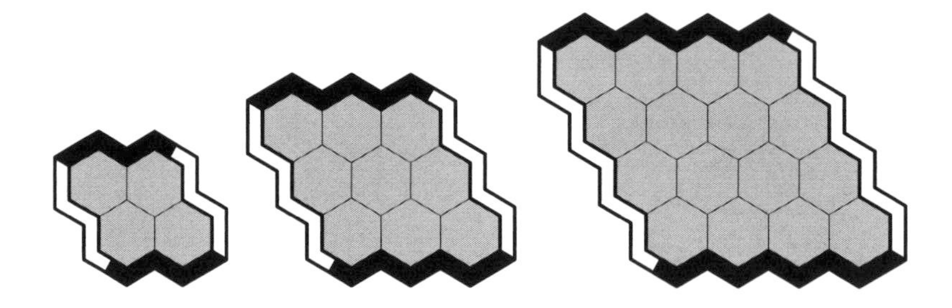

Figure 1.5. Hex boards.

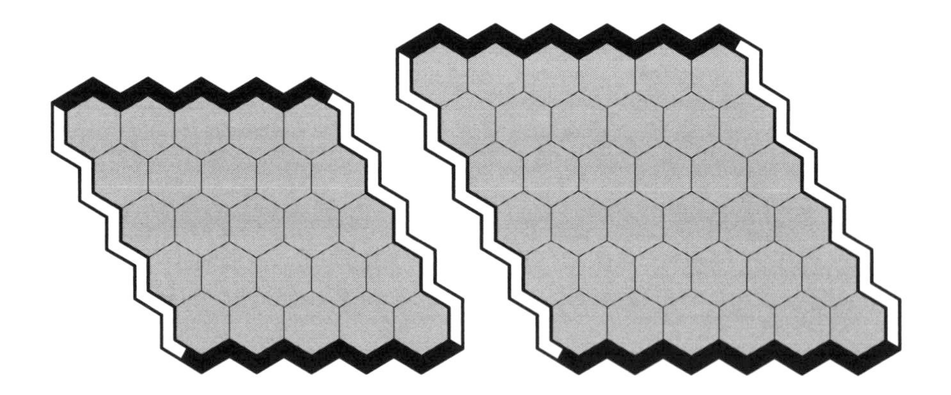

Figure 1.6. More boards.

1.4 balancing the game

In Hex, a strong player usually wins quickly against a weak player. To make games more fun, balance them by allowing the weaker player two or more moves to start, as in Figure 1.7. How would you finish this game?

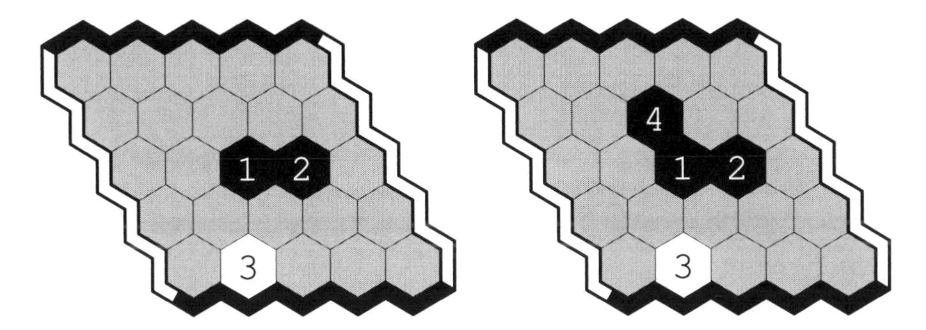

Figure 1.7. White allows Black two moves to start.

When two strong players play, the first player has an advantage. (We will prove this later!) To balance such games, use the *swap rule*:

- the first player makes the first move,
- the second player has the option — which they take if they think the first move is strong — to swap stones and edges with the first player,
- the player whose stone is not on the board makes the next move,
- from then, turns alternate as usual.

Figure 1.8 shows the start of a game of with the swap-rule. To start, Ann is Black, Kim is White. Ann opens 1.B[c3]. Now it is Kim's turn. Kim thinks that Ann's opening move is strong, so Kim swaps. We show this move in the middle diagram by changing the label on the black stone at c3 from 1 to S (for swap). (An S on a stone in a game diagram tells you that that stone was played on move 1 and taken by swap on move 2.) Now Ann is White and Kim is Black and it is Ann's turn. Next Ann plays 3.W[b5]. In game notation, this game starts 1.B[c3] 2.W[swap] 3.W[b5].

Figure 1.3 shows a game in which the second player did not swap. In game notation, that game starts 1.B[c3] 2.W[d3] 3.B[a5].

The swap rule is often used in Hex tournaments, but in this book — unless we say otherwise — we will follow the original Hex rules, so without swap.

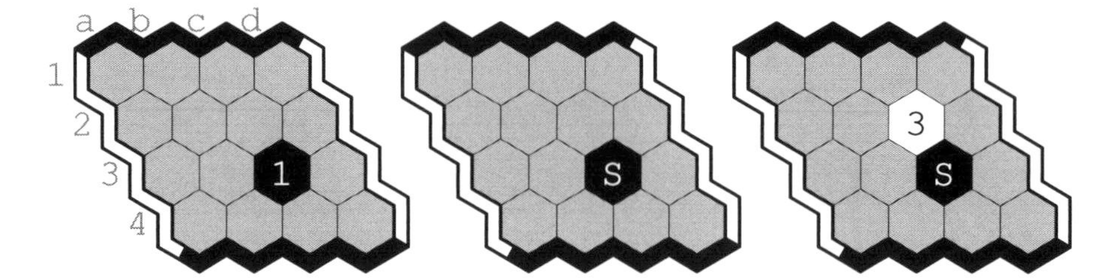

Figure 1.8. Start of a game with the swap rule.

1.5 things to know

As you learn Hex, keep these properties in mind:

- Draws are not possible. (Do you believe this? Can you prove it?) If neither player has yet joined their two edges, then there must be at least one empty cell, so the game continues.
- On $n \times n$ boards, the first player has a winning strategy. Finding such a strategy is easy up to 5×5 boards. Can you do this?
- On $n \times m$ boards with n not equal to m, the player whose edges are closer together has a winning strategy, even if the opponent plays first. Can you find such a strategy?
- The centermost cell is a strong opening move. This is especially noticeable on small boards.
- For arbitrary Hex positions, finding which of the two players has a winning strategy is computationally hard.
- Hex is fun! (This property is best proved by example.)

We will prove some of these properties in later chapters.

1.6 puzzles

Enough chat, let's play! Here are some simple puzzles with Black to play. Can you find all winning moves? Solutions on the next page.

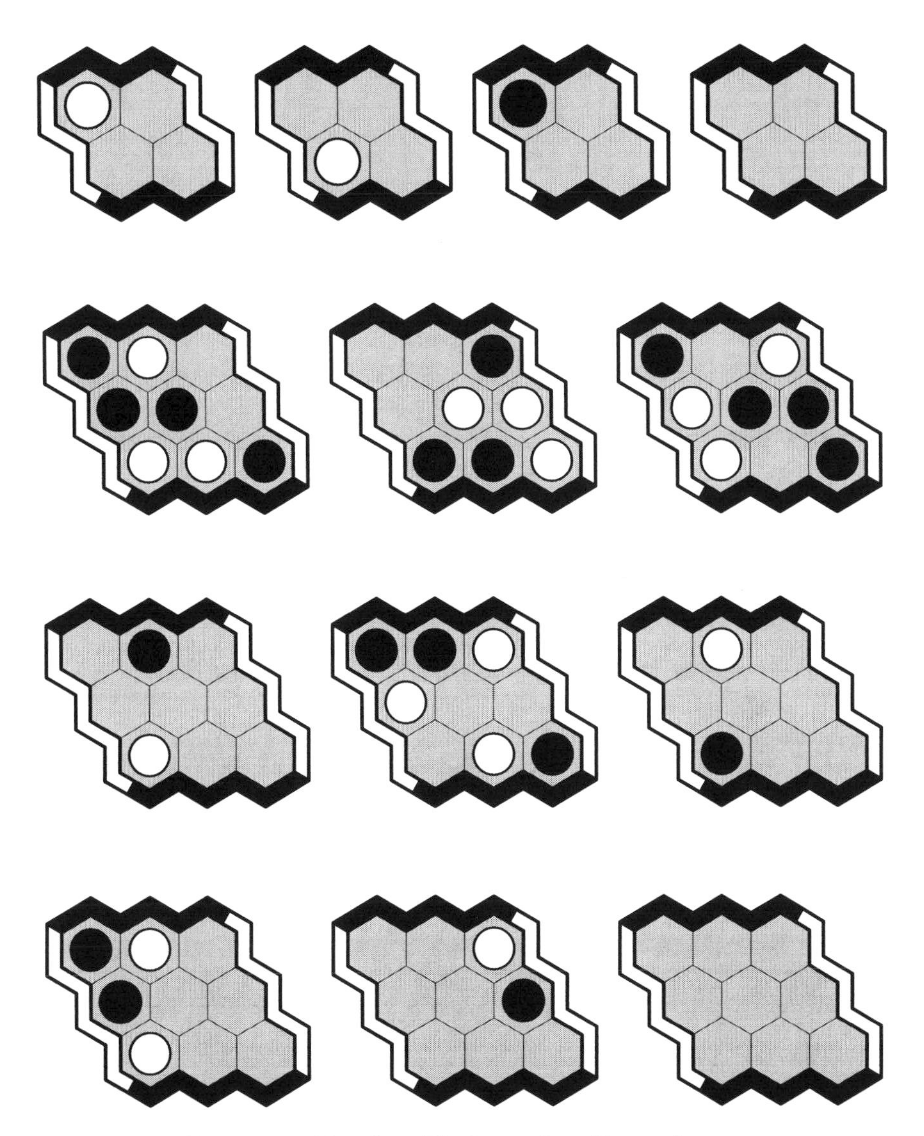

Figure 1.9. Puzzles. Black to play. For each puzzle, find all winning moves.

1.7 solutions

Here are all Black-winning moves. If no move wins, ? shows a move that most prolongs the game. The next chapter helps you find these solutions.

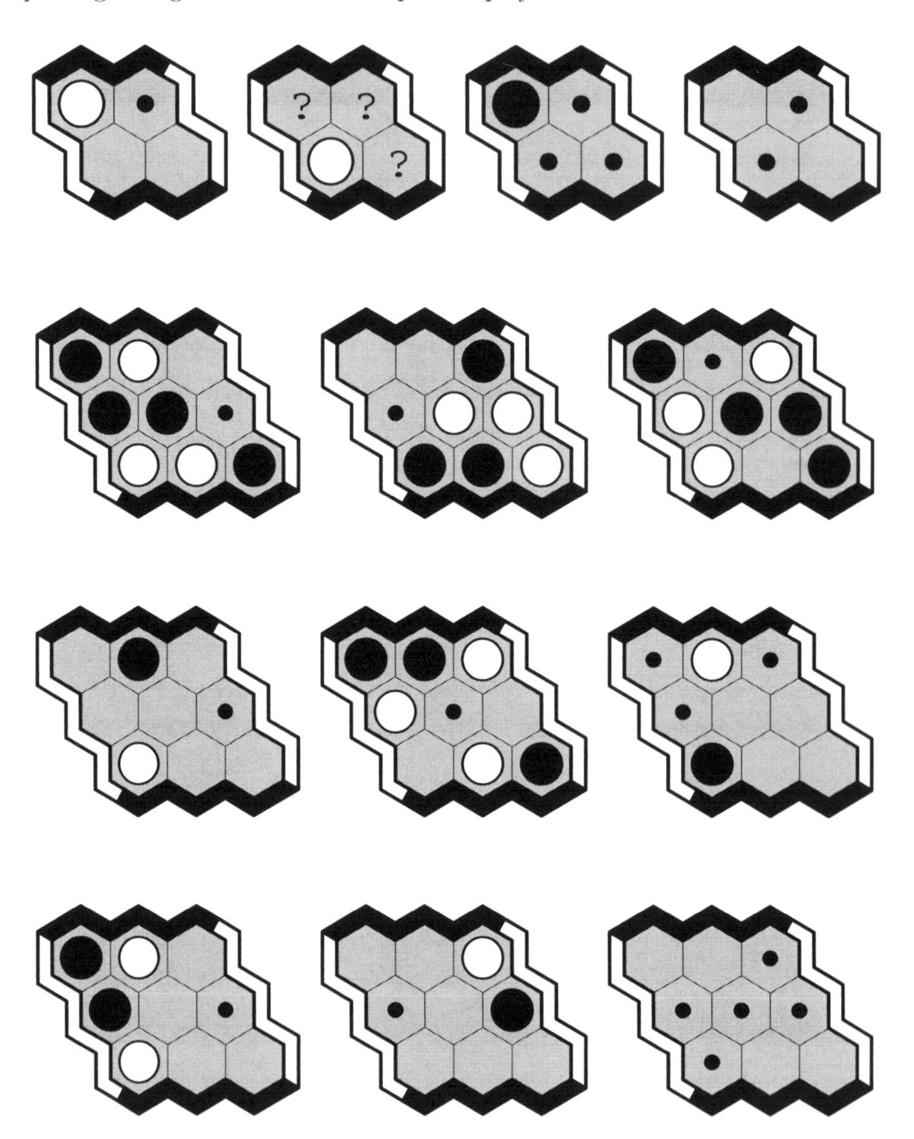

Figure 1.10. All Black-winning moves.

2

basics

It is a happy talent to know how to play.

Ralph Waldo Emerson

Here are some basic tips for playing Hex. Skip this chapter if you are already an expert or would rather learn on your own.

Let's start small. In Figure 2.1, for Black and for the two smallers boards, can you find all winning moves and — for each such move — an accompanying strategy? A *winning move* is the first move of a winning strategy. A *winning strategy* wins against every possible opponent strategy. Answers start on the next page.

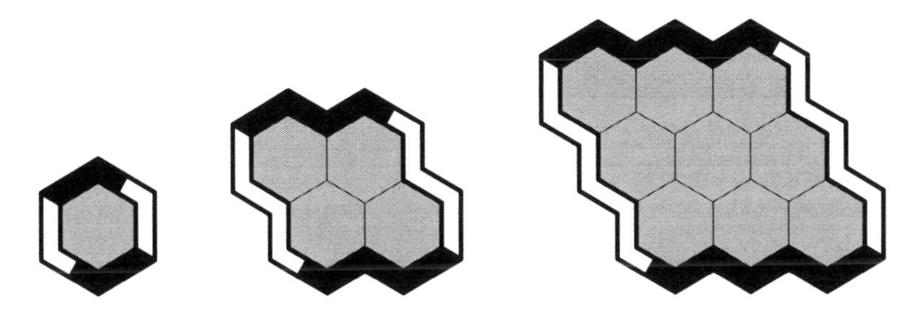

Figure 2.1. Can you find all winning black moves?

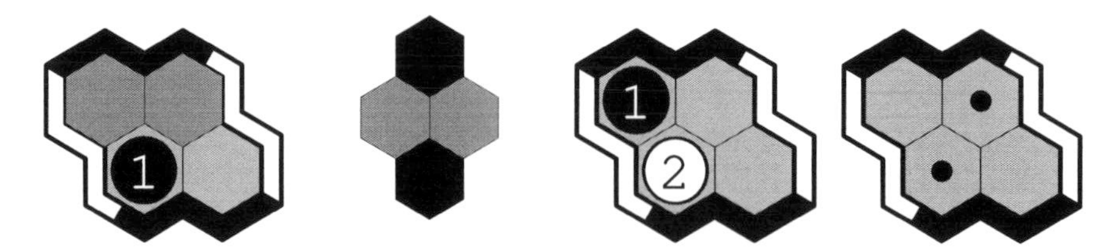

Figure 2.2. For Black: a winning move, the bridge template, a losing move (with winning opponent reply), and all winning moves.

Answers for 1×1 and 2×2 boards. For the 1×1 board the only move wins! For the 2×2 board, the first diagram of Figure 2.2 shows a winning opening move: if White replies at a dark cell, Black takes the other dark cell and wins. In Hex, connection patterns are called *templates*. The template in the second diagram, also appearing in the first diagram — two empty cells between two occupied cells (or cell and edge) — is called the *bridge*. The third diagram shows a winning White reply via a bridge to the right edge to Black's losing opening move. By symmetry — rotate the board — the other two openings are the same as the two we have discussed, so the fourth diagram shows all 2×2 winning black moves.

To find all winning 3×3 empty-board moves, we need some theory.

2.1 block

Consider this advice from Piet Hein:[**25**]

The point of Hex is to block your opponent. This is ... part of the essence of the game, that offense and defense blend together. A barrier against your opponent becomes a path for you. Think of Hex as two labyrinths in combat.

In Figure 2.3 where should White play? Answer on the next page.

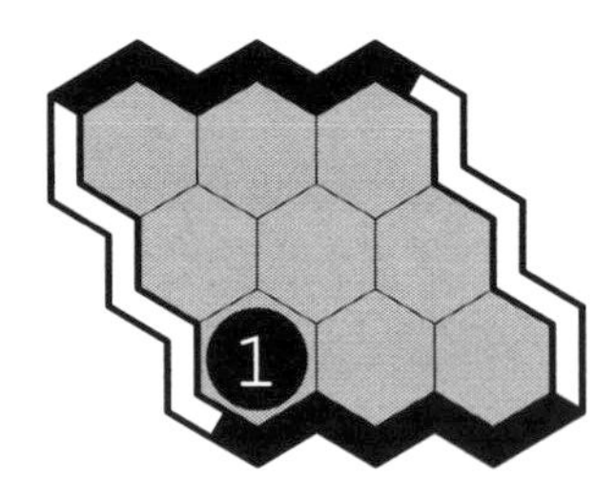

Figure 2.3. Where should White play?

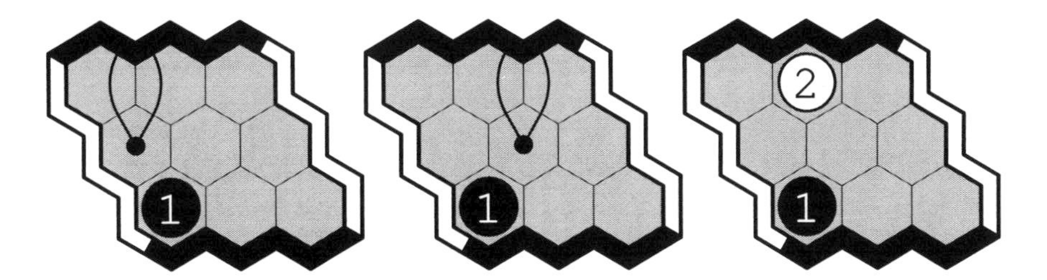

Figure 2.4. White blocks both black threats.

Answer. The first two diagrams in Figure 2.4 each show a three-cell Black-wins threat: play at the dot and then bridge to the top. (A diagram with these spider-like lines showing possible connection paths is sometimes called a *pivot diagram.*) The third diagram shows where White should play: at the only cell that interferes with both threats.

2.2 pairing

White's move in Figure 2.4 merely delays Black's march to victory: Figure 2.5 shows how Black can win. After 2.W[b1] and 3.B[c1], Black has two threats: 5.B[b2] wins immediately, 5.B[c2] wins via a bridge. White can stop only one threat. Like a bridge strategy, Black's strategy here is a *pairing*, a strategy that can be described as a set of pairs of empty cells: whenever your opponent plays in one cell of a pair, you reply at the other cell. In Figure 2.4, after 1.B[a3] Black wins with pairing {{a2, c1}, {a1, b1}, {b2, c2}, {b3, c3}}. The X- and Y-cells in Figure 2.5 show part of this pairing: X is the pair {b2, c2}, Y is the pair {b3, c3}. Can you find a Black-wins pairing in the right diagram of Figure 2.5? Answer on the next page.

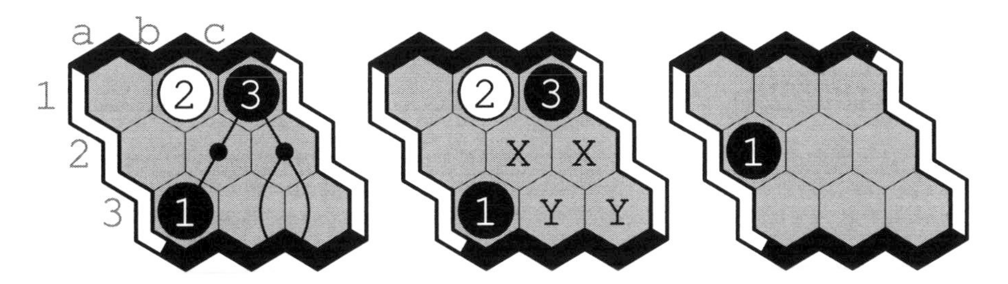

Figure 2.5. (left, middle) 3.B[c1] wins like this.
(right) Can you find a Black-wins pairing?

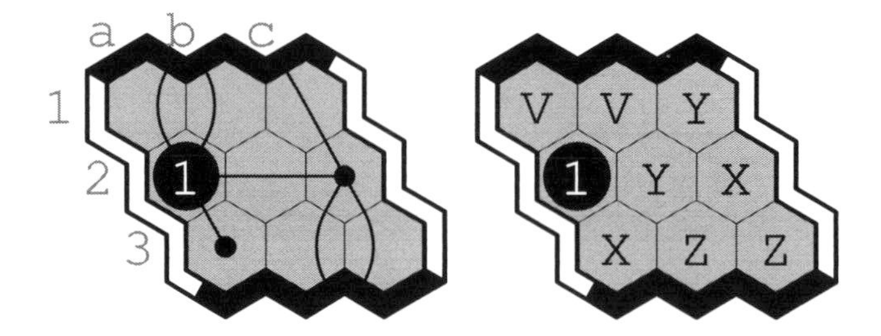

Figure 2.6. A Black-wins pairing.

Answer. Figure 2.6 shows how Black wins in the right diagram of Figure 2.5. Use the {a1, b1} bridge to join a2 to the top. Now Black has two threats, shown by dots: a3, or c2 plus bridges {b2, c1} and {b3, c3}. This strategy is a pairing, as shown in the right diagram.

2.3 3×3 openings

Using what you have learned — bridges, blocking, pairs — can you find all winning opening moves for the 3×3 board? Use the empty boards below to try your ideas. Answer on the next page.

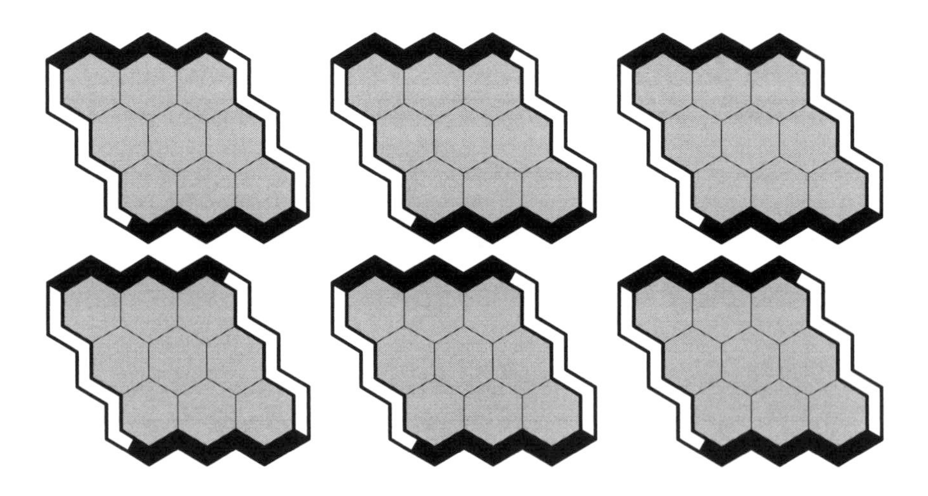

Figure 2.7. Try your ideas.

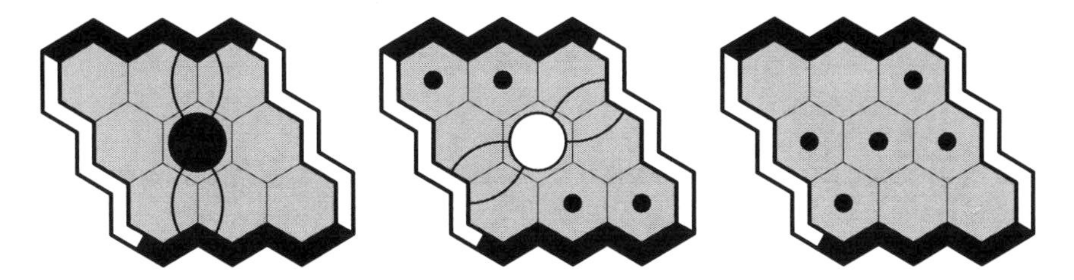

Figure 2.8. Center opening wins, four black losing openings, all black winning openings.

Answer. Figures 2.4 and 2.5 show that the obtuse corner opening wins. Figure 2.6 shows that the opponent-edge-middle opening wins. Figure 2.8 (left) shows that the center opening wins. Figure 2.8 (middle) shows that all other openings lose. So we have all 3×3 winning openings (right).

2.4 safe connections

The winning strategy in Figure 2.6 consists of several cell-to-cell or cell-to-edge templates, also called *safe connections*, since the player can connect even if the opponent moves next. The bridge, with only two empty cells, is the simplest template. Figure 2.9 shows four third-row templates that each join a stone to the edge: the 3-2-1 (with 3, 2, 1 cells respectively in the templates's rows), 3-3-2, 3-3-2b, and 4-3-2. There are other naming conventions: 4-3-2 is also called *ziggurat* after the shape of ancient terraced buildings, called III-1-a by HexWiki [**13**], and called A-3 by Seymour [**38**].

Fun fact: safe connections also feature in the game of Go, where bridges are called *miai* (pronounced mee-eye), meaning *equal options*.

For each template in Figure 2.9, can you find a strategy that safely joins the stone to the bottom? Answer on the next page.

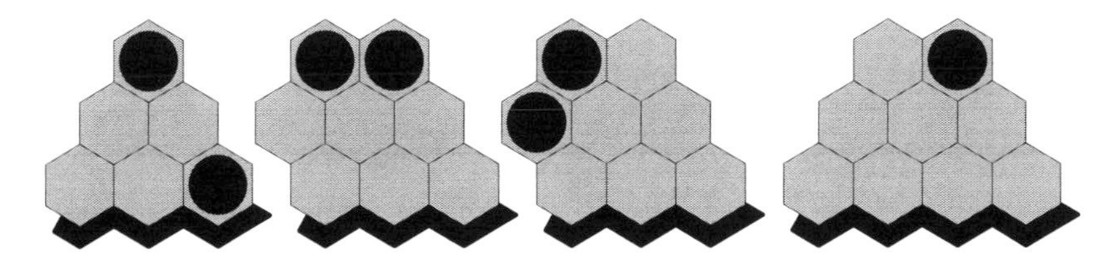

Figure 2.9. From left: 3-2-1, 3-3-2, 3-3-2b, 4-3-2 edge templates. For each, find a strategy.

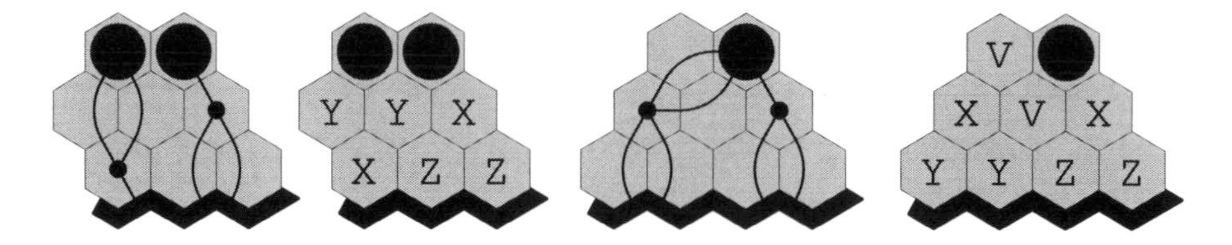

Figure 2.10. 3-2-2 and 4-3-2 connection strategies.

Answer. We leave it to you to find a strategy for the 3-2-1 and 3-3-2b safe connections. Figure 2.10 shows strategies for 3-3-2 and 4-3-2 that safely joins Black's stone group at top to the bottom, even if White moves next.

2.5 6×6 puzzle

Let's apply what we have learned to a 6×6 puzzle. In Figure 2.11, where should Black play? Remember Hein's advice: block the opponent. A *winning path* for a player is a set of empty cells that joins her two edges. One way to block the opponent is to play at a cell on one of her *shortest* winning paths. But some such cells block better than others.

Figure 2.11 gives you a hint: we have shaded each cell on any shortest White-wins path. Each Black move that is *not* at a shaded cell loses easily. (White can then play at any dot in Figure 2.12 and use three bridges.) Which of the nine shaded cells in Figure 2.11 is a good move for Black? Read on ...

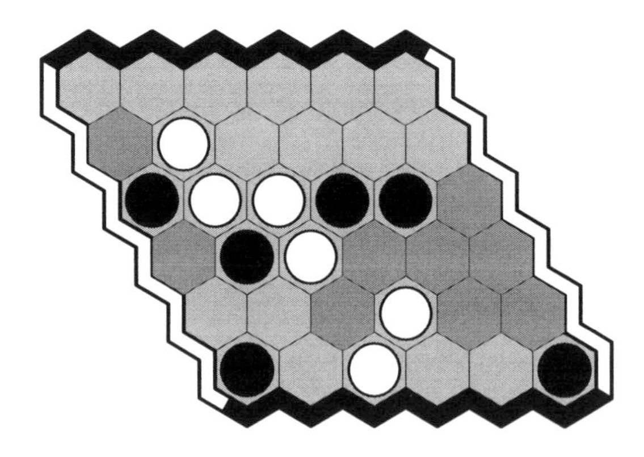

Figure 2.11. Where should Black play?

2.6 win-threats

To avoid defeat, block each opponent win-threat. The shaded cells in the top diagrams of Figure 2.12 each show a White win-threat. Black must block each threat by playing at a cell that is shaded in both diagrams. There are five such cells, shown in the bottom diagram. Do any of these five black moves win? Answer on the next page.

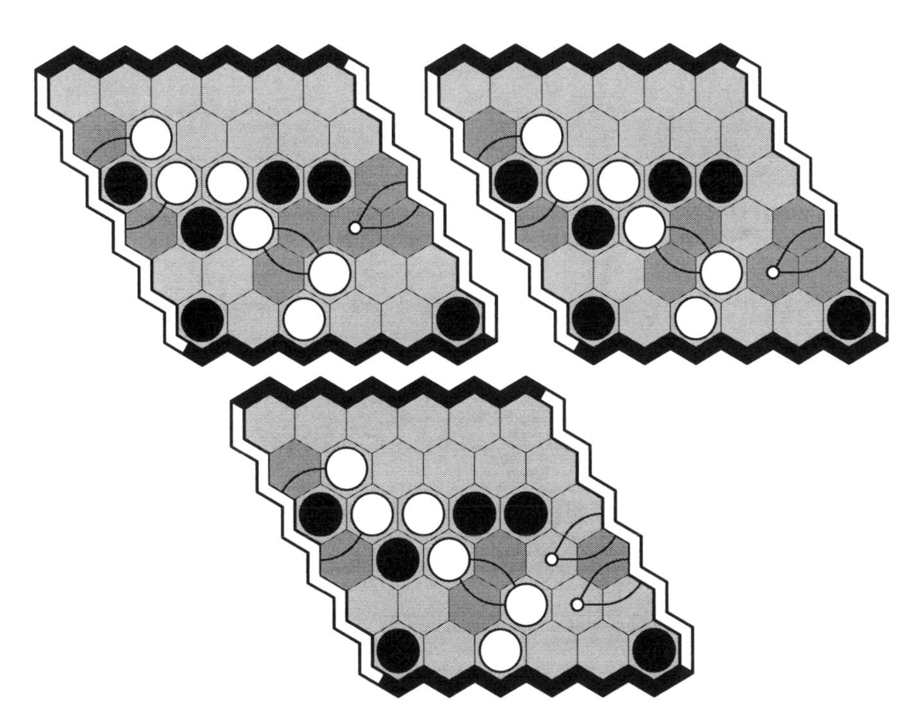

Figure 2.12. To interfere with the two white threats at top, Black must make one of the five moves shown at bottom.

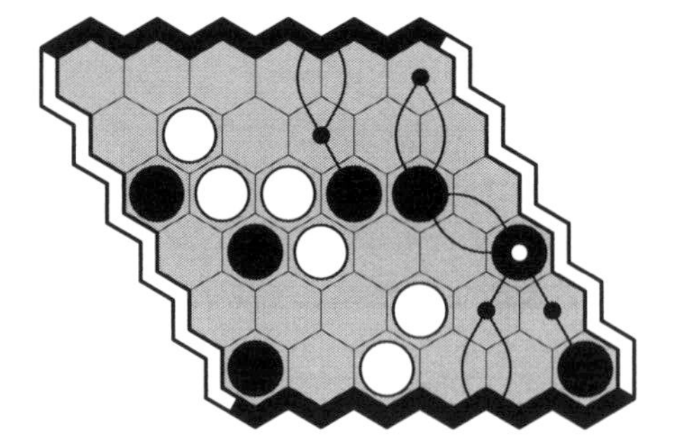

Figure 2.13. A winning black move.

Answer. All five black moves win. The four moves in the two white bridges of Figure 2.12 win slowly: in each case White can restore the bridge but Black can still win. The move in Figure 2.13 wins quickly: join the bottom with a 3-2-1, join the top with a bridge and a 3-2-2.

2.7 Fourth row safe connection

Sometimes you cannot stop all opponent win-threats. In Figure 2.14 with White to play, who wins? Hint: see Figure 2.15. Answer below.

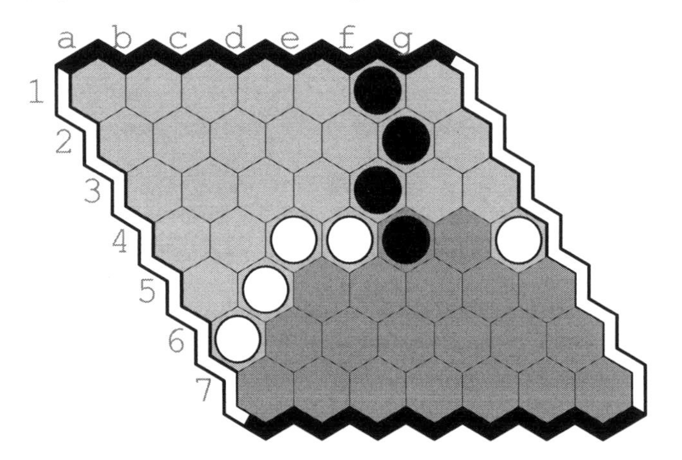

Figure 2.14. White to play: who wins?

Answer. Black wins with the dark cells in Figure 2.14, a fourth row safe connection we call 7-6-5-2. If White plays any of {e5, e6, e7, f4, f5, f6, f7, g5, g6, g7} then Black can reply at d5 as in the left diagram of Figure 2.15 and finish the win by maintaining the resulting 4-3-2 connection. Similarly, if White plays d7 then Black can reply at e5. And if White plays any of {a7, b6, b7, c5, c6, c7, d5, d6} then Black can reply at f5.

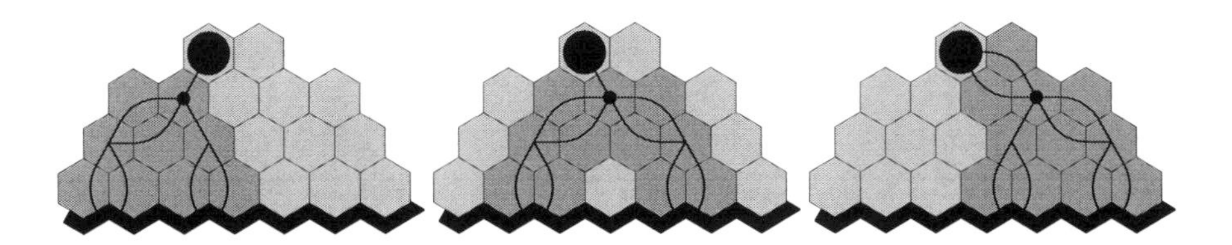

Figure 2.15. Three threats form the 7-6-5-2.

2.8 weak, safe, super connection

If you are new to Hex, skip this section for now: come back to it when you are comfortable recognizing templates.

Figure 2.16 shows two kinds of connection. The dark cells {a5, a6} form a white bridge between the left edge and b5. This is a *safe connection*: White can force the connection even if Black plays next. The dark cells {e2, f1, f2} form a connection threat between d3 and g1. This is a *weak connection*: White can force the connection only by playing in the connection region {e2, f1, f2} before Black plays there.

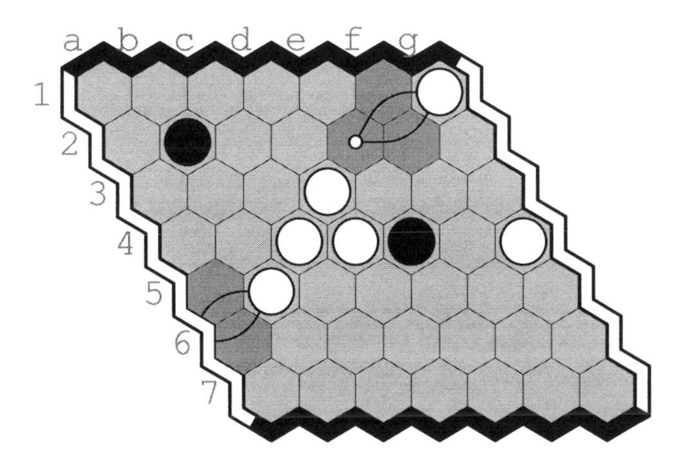

Figure 2.16. weak and safe connections

The shaded cell set S ={a3, a4, a5, a6, b3, b4, c3} in Figure 2.17 form a new kind of connection we have not seen before, a *super connection* between the left edge and White's group at {b5, c4, d3, d4}. White can ignore an initial Black attack into S. Why? This super connection is formed from *three* non-intersecting weak connections: {a5}, {a6}, and {b3,a3,a4,c3,b4}. Black's initial attack misses two non-intersecting weak connections, which form a safe connection. Any Black attack into S still leaves a safe connection. Only after Black attacks S a second time will White have to reply in S in order to preserve the connection.

To use a weak connection, a player must play there before the opponent. To use a safe connection, a player can wait until the opponent attacks it before replying. To use a super connection, a player can wait until the opponent attacks it two times before replying.

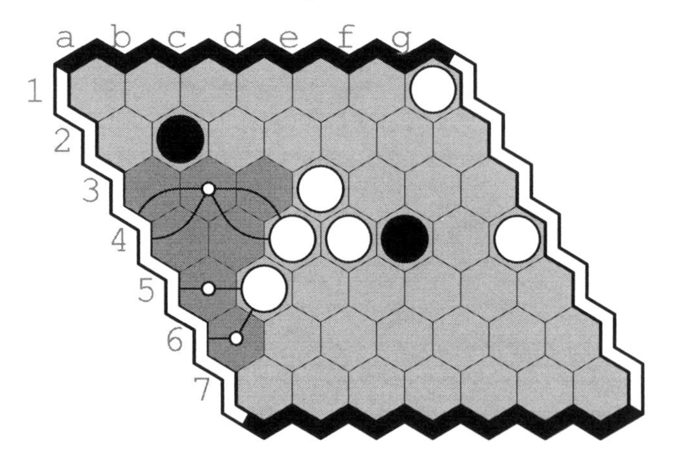

Figure 2.17. A super connection formed by 3 non-intersecting weak connections.

In Figure 2.17, where should Black play? The shaded cells {a5, a6, e2, f1, f2} in Figure 2.16 form a white win-threat, so Black must play at one of these five cells. But only one wins! Can you find it? Hint: it won't be either a5 or a6, which are in the super connection in Figure 2.17. You have three remaining cells to check. Answer on the next page.

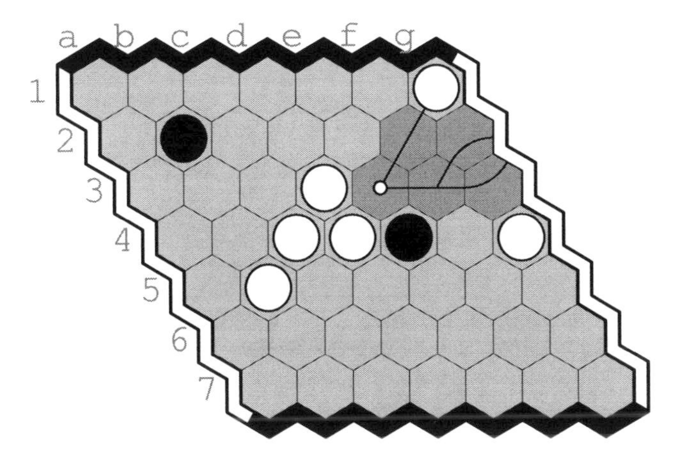

Figure 2.18. Another white win-threat.

Answer. So far the mustplay region is {e2, f1, f2}. Figure 2.18 shows another white win-threat. The intersection of this threat and our mustplay is {f2}: every other black move loses. For example, if Black plays a5 — in the super white connection in Figure 2.17 — then White can reply at e3 and win. So, every black move except f2 loses. Does this black move win?

Yes! Figure 2.19 shows the winning move and the resulting connection pattern. The template in the top two rows is called a *ladder*, because the move pattern that forms as the opponent tries to stop it — shown by the lines — looks like a ladder. Ladders are common in Hex and — you guessed it — also in Go.

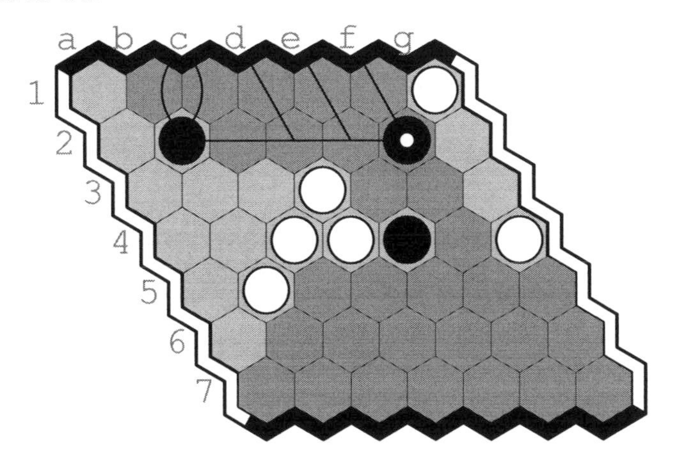

Figure 2.19. Black wins with this ladder.

2.9 blunders

It can be fun — or painful! — to look back and analyze a game. Obviously, you would want to change any *blunder*, a losing move made when a winning move was available. How many blunders were made in the game in Figure 2.20?

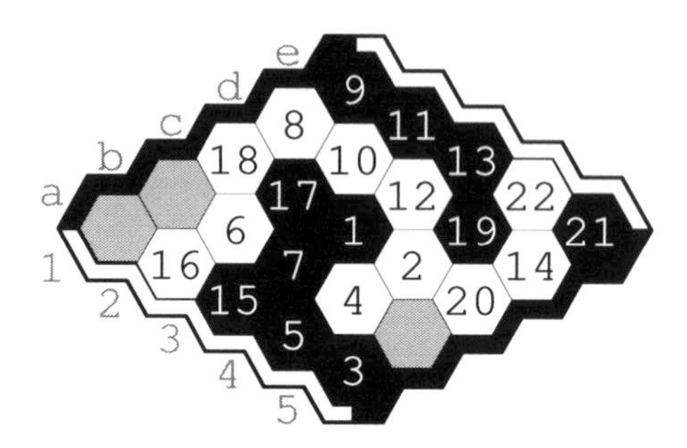

Figure 2.20. Can you find all blunders?

After 1.B[c3], Black joins both top and bottom with a 4-3-2 connection, so move 1 wins and is not a blunder. So White has no winning move 2, so move 2 is not a blunder. Next we expect move 3.B[b4] — which restores the bottom connection after 2.W[c4] — instead of 3.B[a5]: is this a winning move? If not then it is the game's first blunder.

As shown in Figure 2.21, the game has exactly three blunders. For each, can you find a winning move? Answer on the next page.

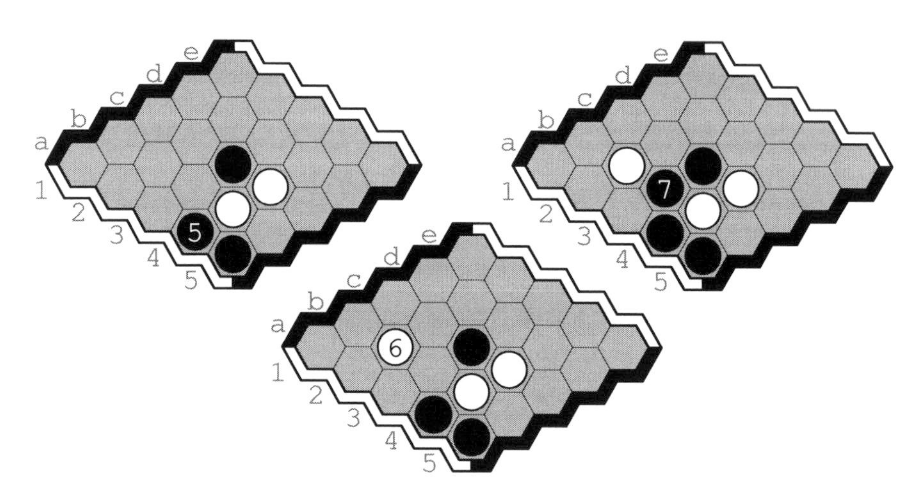

Figure 2.21. The game's blunders. In each case, find a winning move. Answer on the next page.

Answer. Each diagram of Figure 2.22 shows the only winning move for that position. For example, in the first diagram, Black's only winning move is d3. We leave it to you to find winning strategies that go with these three winning moves, and to show that these three moves — moves 5, 6 and 7 in Figure 2.20 — were the game's only blunders.

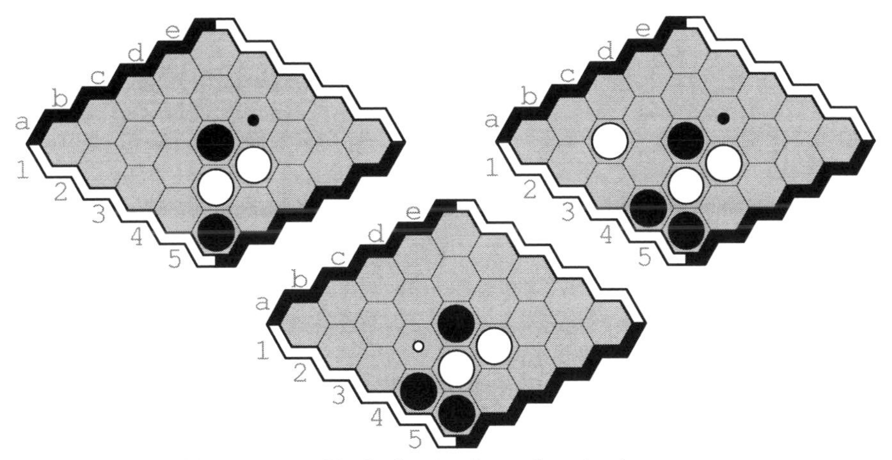

Figure 2.22. Each dot is the only winning move.

Now you can play Hex! If you want more practise, try to find all winning opening moves on the 4×4 and 5×5 boards. And try the puzzles in the next section.

2.10 puzzles

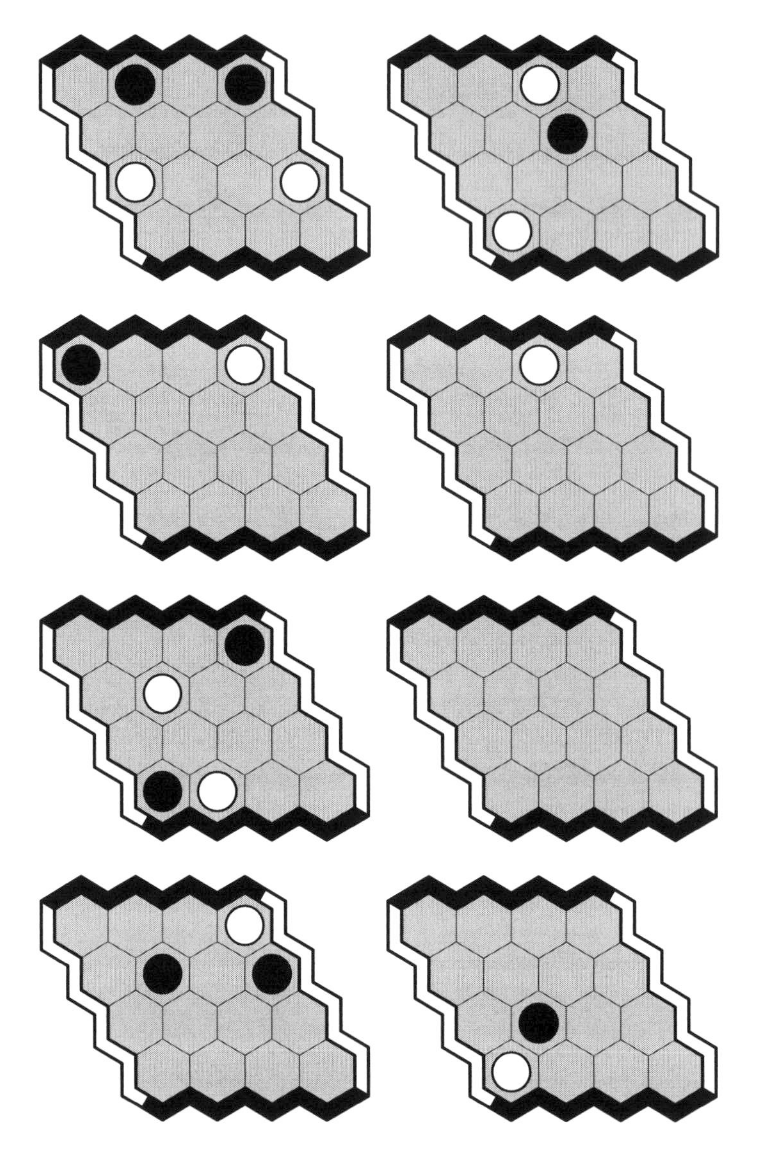

Figure 2.23. Find all winning moves. Top 3 rows: Black to play. Bottom row: White to play.

2.11 solutions

Let's solve the first puzzle.

Figure 2.24 shows two White win-threats: use {b2, b3, c2, c3, d2} or {a4, b3, b4, c3, c4}. These threats intersect on {b3, c3}, so Black must play one of these two moves, otherwise White can win. Can Black win with one or both of these moves?

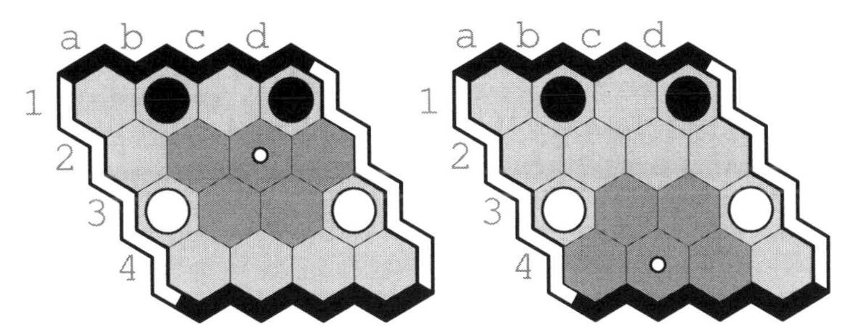

Figure 2.24. Two White win-threats.

Yes, both moves win. Figure 2.25 shows two Black win-strategies: play b2 and then bridge to the bottom and to the top via b1 or d1, or play b3 and then bridge to the bottom and to the top via d1.

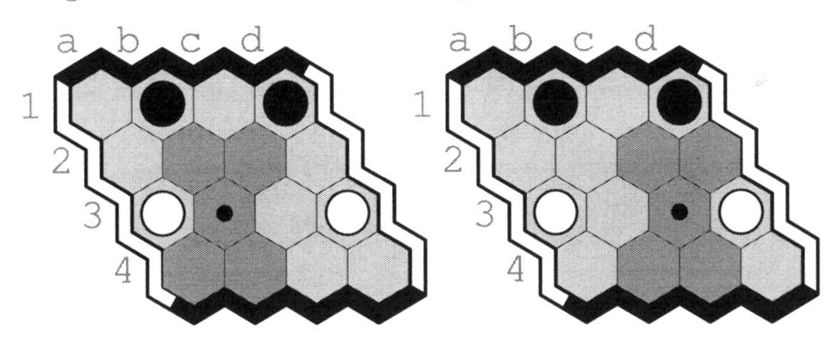

Figure 2.25. Two Black win-strategies.

Now you can try the other puzzles.

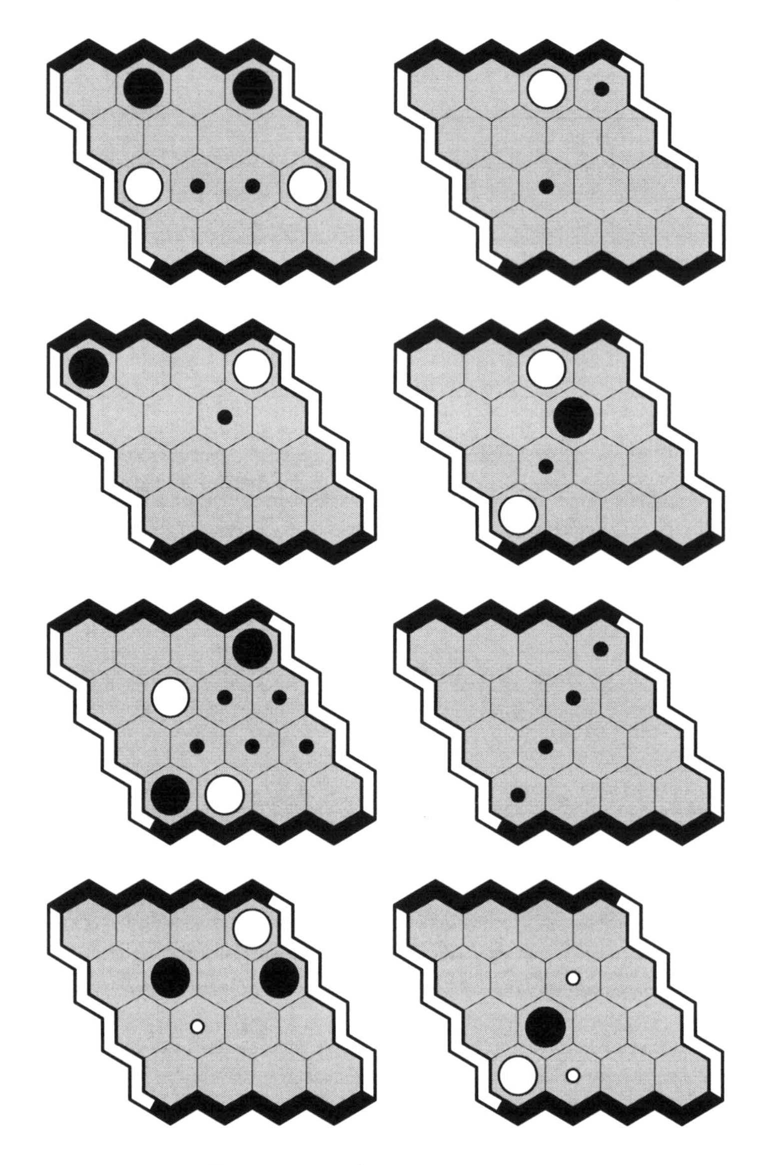

Figure 2.26. All winning moves.

3
how Hex began

It takes a village to raise a child.

African proverb

You might have wondered ... where did Hex come from?

3.1 Hein's game

Hex was invented in 1942 by Piet Hein, a Danish engineer, inventor, designer and poet [**24, 26**]. (In 1966 Hein was featured in, and on the cover of, Life magazine as a celebrity polymath, well known for eclectic designs — tables, chairs, a candlestick-holder shaped like the Big Dipper, a traffic superellipse rather than a traffic circle — and for pithy poems called grooks: *problems worthy of attack prove their worth by hitting back* [**28**].)

Hex came from the war, born of necessity. In 1941, after Germany invaded Denmark and Norway, Hein — an outspoken anti-Nazi — went underground. Wanting income but needing to stay hidden, Hein recalled an idea.

Years earlier, inspired by the then-unsolved four-color problem — can every planar map be colored with at most four colors? — Hein had noticed the property shown at the top of Figure 3.1: if a line drawn inside a rectangle joins two opposite edges and another such line joins the other two edges, then the lines must cross.

Imagine two opposing armies, each split into two groups, with the four groups aligned alternately around a four-edged territory. Each army wants to unite its two groups but, by the crossing-lines property, only one army can succeed. On a turn in Hein's game, an army occupies an empty cell of the territory grid. As you can see in the middle diagram of Figure 3.1, a rectangular grid allows the two armies to block each other. Hein did not want draws, so he had abandoned this game idea.

In 1942 Hein saw how to salvage his game idea. In a rectangular grid, four cells can meet at a point. Four is an even number, so the cells around a point can be alternately occupied by the two players, creating a deadlock. To avoid draws, Hein used a hexagonal grid as in the bottom of Figure 3.1. On these grids deadlocks cannot occur: only three cells can meet at a point, so if two paths end in two cells that meet at a point, exactly one of the paths can continue by taking the third cell. Hein picked board size 11×11 and called the game Polygon. We now call it Hex.

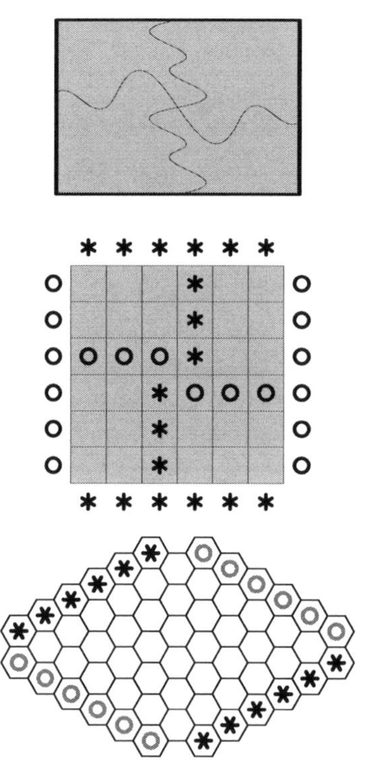

Figure 3.1. Hex evolution, from top. Each curve joins two opposite edges, so the curves must cross. On a square grid, armies can block each other. Finished board.

3.2 Lindhard's puzzles

Hein — an amazing designer but a weak player — was unsure whether Polygon would be fun to play, so he asked some chess players to try it out. They were excited: in spite of its simple rules, the game required strategy and tactics and exploring long lines of play — just as in chess.

To market the game, Hein wrote Polygon columns — see Figures 3.2 and 3.3 — for the Danish newspaper *Politiken*. The newspaper in turn published 50-sheet pads of Polygon boards, with Hein and the paper splitting the profit.

Within a year Polygon reached Sudoku-like popularity, with 20,000 game pads sold. Hein crowd-sourced his puzzles: most were composed by Jens Lindhard, then a 22-year old physics student and chess master, later a professor who worked closely with Neils Bohr. Others were inspired by readers, including a young math student named Karen Thorborg. The columns appeared from December 1942 until August 1943, when Hein finally fled to Argentina. As quickly as it had appeared, the game vanished.

POLYGON

A puzzle for new players. Among the many letters we receive from readers enjoying Polygon are those asking that we make our puzzles more difficult ... accompanied of course by incorrect solutions to earlier puzzles!
This is clear evidence that Polygon is challenging: just when you think you have found a clever move, you run the risk of being not so clever. Perhaps the opposite also holds: if you think you are a poor Polygon player, your cautious self-appraisal might serve you well.

Puzzle 34. An easy problem, White to play and win, with a unique winning move. Try your solution against a worthy opponent! You should be able to win against any Black strategy.

Figure 3.2. Polygon column, March 17, 1943. Translation RBH and Bjarne Toft. © Politiken.

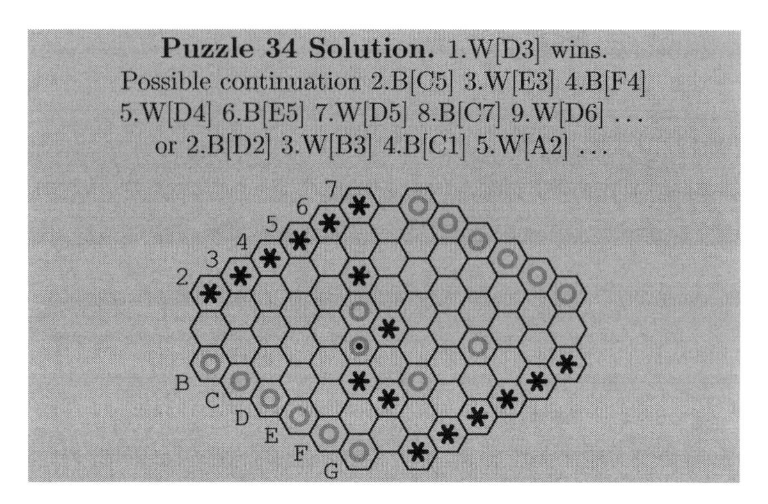

Figure 3.3. From Polygon column March 20 1943. Translation RBH. © Politiken.

3.3 across the ocean

After the war, Hein lived for a time in New York, where he tried to promote Polygon. Parker Brothers heard about the game, renamed it Hex, and published it as a box set in 1950.

Meanwhile, John Nash — a Princeton University game theory student whose Ph.D. thesis later won him a Nobel Prize — discovered the game (perhaps independently of Hein: see the chapter on further reading.) Early in 1949 he told his interim supervisor David Gale about a game that could be played on the intersection points of a checkerboard with diagonals added as in Figure 3.4. Nash was excited: he could prove that the first player can win! (We will show you this proof in the next chapter.)

Gale was intrigued. He saw that the board was equivalent to an array of hexagons and thought that the game might be fun to play, so that day he built a 14×14 board. Gale left his board in the math department common room, and the game soon became popular.

3.4 Gardner's column and Nash's lesson

In 1956 the science writer Martin Gardner wrote a story on hexaflexagons — make-it-yourself folding paper toys — for *Scientific American.* The story was so popular that the magazine hired Gardner to write a monthly column on recreational mathematics. Looking for column ideas, Gardner heard about Hex and wrote Parker Brothers, who put him in touch with Hein, Claude

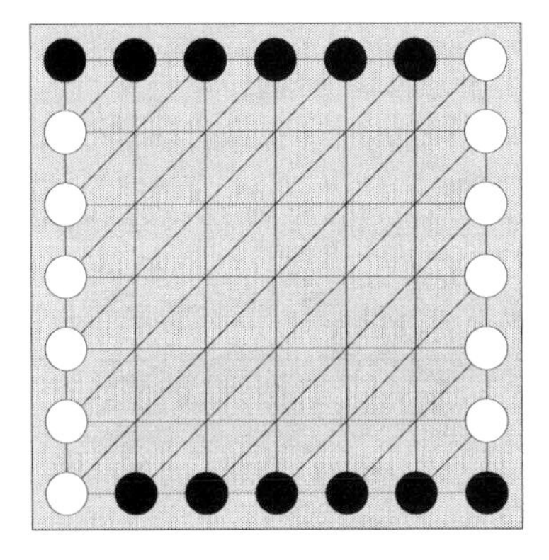

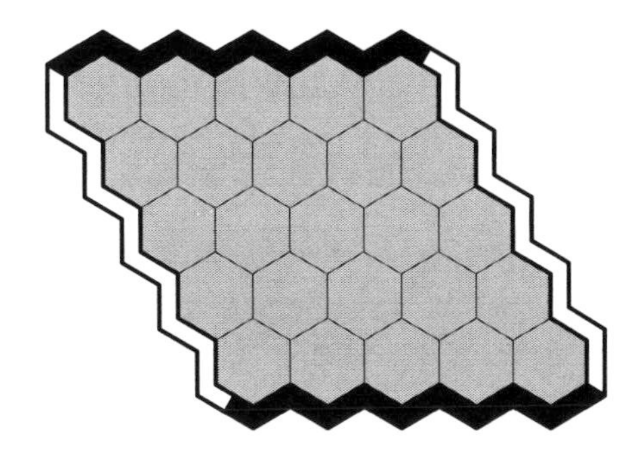

Figure 3.4. Nash's description of the game board. Gale's equivalent board.

Shannon and others. And in March, Gardner ran into Nash in the New York University library.

Gardner invited Nash to his apartment, where they spent an evening discussing Hex. Among other things, Nash showed Gardner which 4×4 opening moves win. Let's look at that problem: for the board in Figure 3.5, can you find all winning Black moves? And for each, a winning strategy?

Before we begin our Hex analysis, notice that symmetry will save us some work. The empty 4×4 board has 16 cells, but 180-degree rotation yields the same board, so we need try only the 8 cells in the top two rows of Figure 3.5. For Black, which opening moves win?

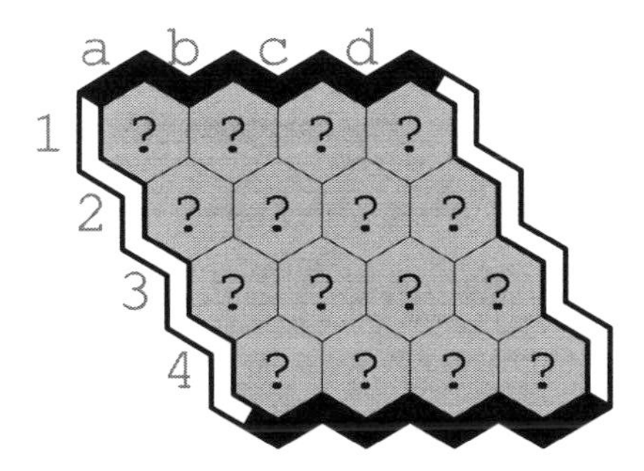

Figure 3.5. Black to play. Which opening moves win?

The left diagram in Figure 3.6 shows a winning move: the black stone joins top with a bridge and joins the bottom with a 4-3-2 connection, shown with shaded cells (the template has 4 cells along the edge, 3 in the next row, 2 in the next row). The right diagram shows five losing opening moves: each loses to the same white reply. The bottom diagram shows another losing black move. (After 1.B[d2] and 2.W[b3], White wins on move 4 with either of the white dots d1 or c4. The lines show possible final winning paths. The letters show that this is also a pairing strategy.) So the last of the eight opening black moves to consider is d1, the obtuse corner: who wins then?

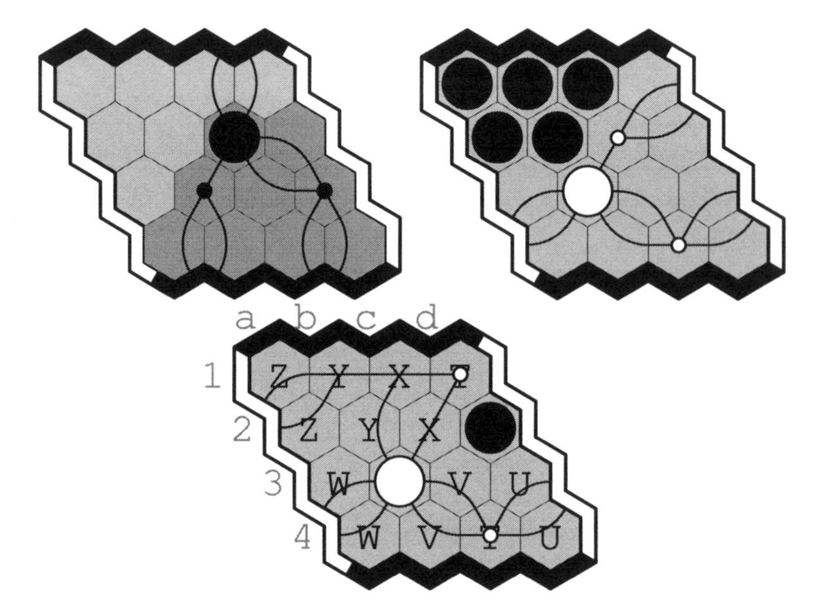

Figure 3.6. A winning move (left). Five losing black moves (right). Another losing black move.

Look at the top diagram in Figure 3.7. White must play at one of the five shaded cells, otherwise Black replies at c3 and wins.

The next two diagrams show how Black can win after a white move to d2 or c3 or c4 (left) or c2 (right). So, to finish our analysis of all 4×4 opening moves, we have only this question from the bottom diagram: after White replies at b4, how does Black win? Answer on the next page.

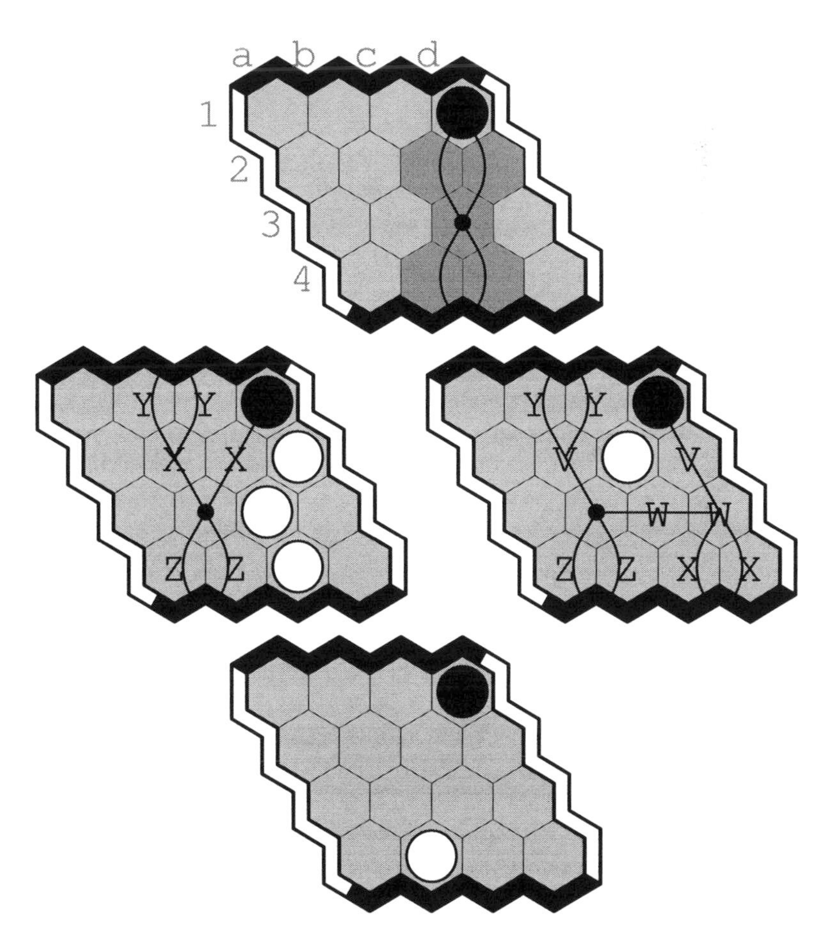

Figure 3.7. (top) White must reply at one of these five cells. (next two) These four white replies lose. (bottom) How does Black win?

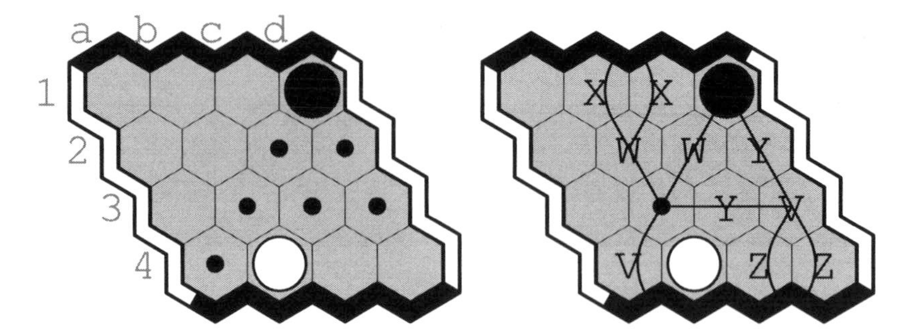

Figure 3.8. After 1.B[d1] 2.W[b4], these black moves win (left) and 3.B[b3] wins like this (right).

Figure 3.8 shows six different winning black moves in this position, together with the strategy after 3.B[b3] — one of the simpler wins. That ends our 4×4 analysis: the only winning opening moves are the four cells on the short diagonal.

During their evening conversation, Nash also showed Gardner some variations on Hex, including Reverse Hex (played on a Hex board: whoever joins their two edges *loses*) and Triangle (played on a triangular board covered with hexagons as in Figure 3.9: whoever joins the three edges wins). Nash credited John Milnor — another mathematician who was a grad student at Princeton with Nash — with inventing Triangle.

(Triangle was invented independently by mathematicians Charles Titus and Craige Schensted at the University of Michigan around 1953. They called the game Y, after the shape of winning stone sets, for example Black's winning Y-shape in Figure 3.9. We will say more in the chapter on Y.)

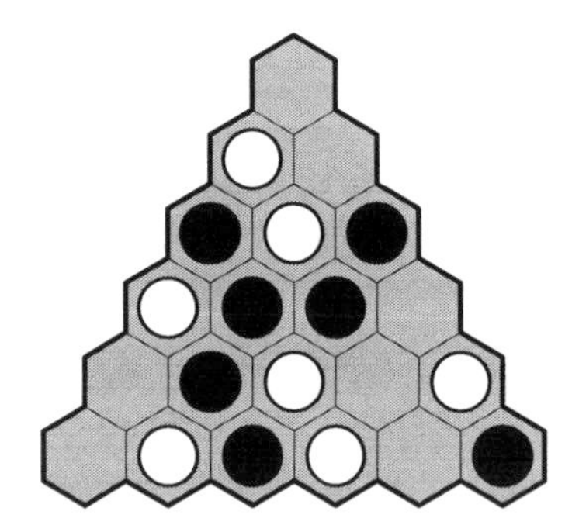

Figure 3.9. Triangle, also called Y. Black's group touches all three edges, so Black wins.

That evening Nash also showed Gardner how to win as first player on the 5×5 board. (Can you figure out how to do that? Answer below in Figure 3.10.) And he explained his beautiful proof that, for any $n\times n$ board, the first player can win.

Gardner's column — *Concerning the game of Hex, which may be played on the tiles of the bathroom floor* — appeared in the July 1957 issue of *Scientific American* and proved popular. Fifteen years after its creation, Hex was being played around the world.

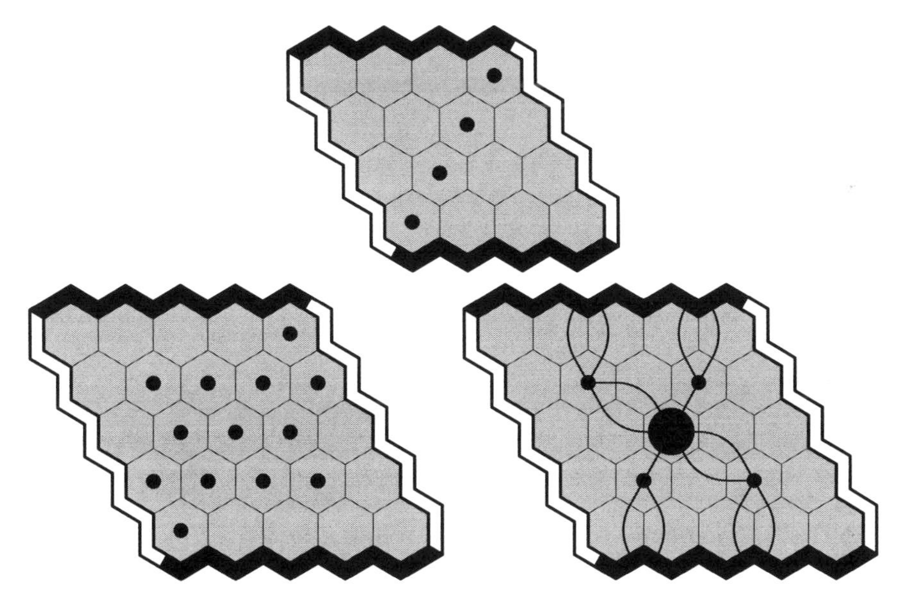

Figure 3.10. All 4×4 and 5×5 winning opening Black moves. A 5×5 center-opening winning strategy: join each edge with a 4-3-2 connection.

3.5 puzzles

On the next page are some Hex puzzles with White to play. The bottom left puzzle is by Karen Thorborg. For each puzzle, find as many winning moves as you can. One puzzle has no winning move: for that puzzle, find a move that prolongs the game as much as possible.

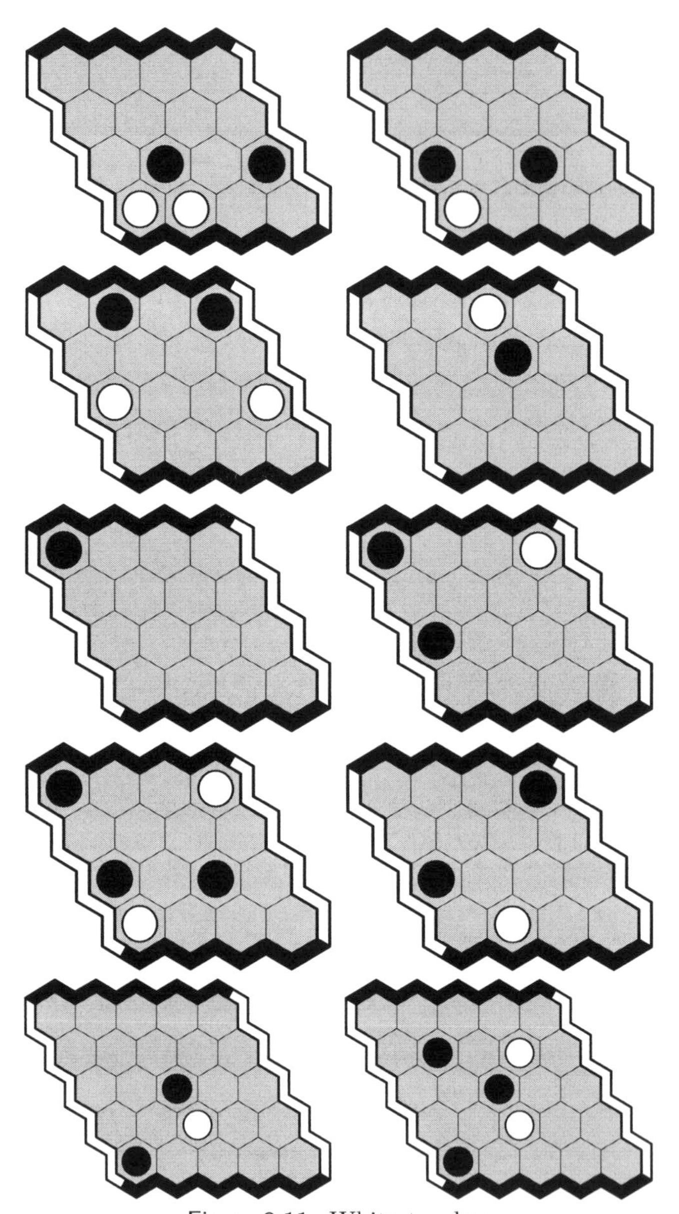

Figure 3.11. White to play.

3.6 solutions

If no move wins, ? shows a move that most prolongs the game.

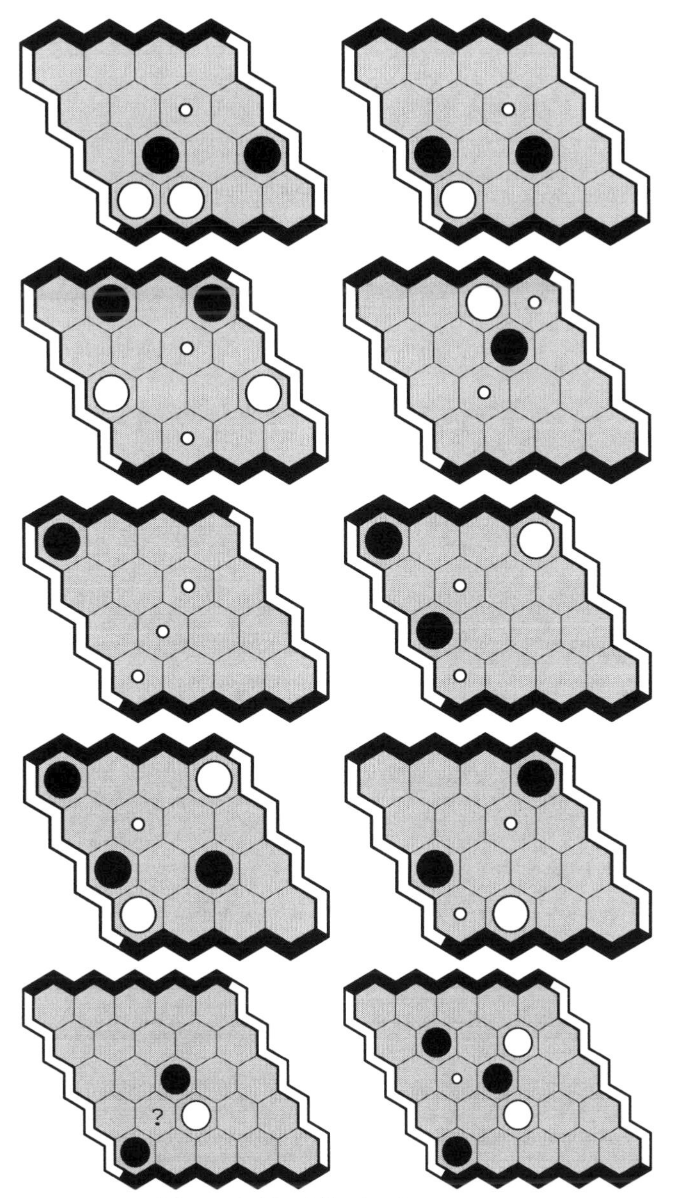

Figure 3.12. All winning moves.

4

first player wins

Strong players of other games have taken up [11×11 Hex] and played it for the 3-4 months it has existed. They believe that it would take years to consider enough lines of play to be reasonably sure to win. ... A game between strong players can take an hour or two. But [the first player] can win.

Piet Hein, February 1943

In a public tutorial in Copenhagen in 1943, Piet Hein mentioned the property of his new game that so excited John Nash six years later: for any $n \times n$ board, the first player has a winning strategy (see [**24**]).

Why is this remarkable? Consider chess and Go. Both games have been played for centuries. For each game, there is overwhelming circumstantial evidence that the first player should win or draw. But no one has proved this.

In this chapter we will show you that in Hex the first player can win. We start by showing you two Hex properties.

4.1 no draws

Here is our first theorem: Hex has no draws, every game ends with a win.

To prove this remarkable property, assume that it is your turn in a Hex game. Neither you nor your opponent has yet won. We want to show that there must be at least one empty cell, in which case you can move and the game continues. Actually, we will show the contrapositive: every filled Hex board has either a set of black stones joining the two black edges or a set of white stones joining the two white edges. Why is this last statement true?

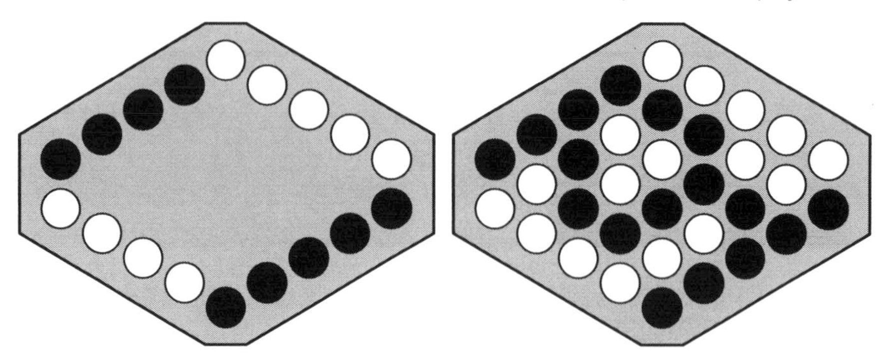

Figure 4.1. Place stones along the four board edges and then fill each interior cell.

Here is a proof from the classic text *On Signals and Noise* by John R. Pierce, the engineer — and science writer — who gave the transistor its name [**34**]. As in Figure 4.1, put stones on the edges of a Hex board and then fill all cells. Next, as in Figure 4.2, draw a path at the left acute corner of the board that goes between the B-stone (Black stone) from the top left edge and the W-stone from the bottom left edge, and continue the path, always keeping a B-stone on the left and a W-stone on the right.

In detail, the procedure is this. Whenever the path's current line segment reaches a three-stone junction, label these three stones X (the W-stone to the right of the segment), Y (the B-stone to the left of the segment), and Z (the stone that the segment is heading towards). If Z is a B-stone, the next segment turns to the right and passes between Y and Z. If Z is a W-stone, the next segment turns to the left and passes between X and Z. It follows immediately that (1) the path cannot end at such a junction and (2) the new

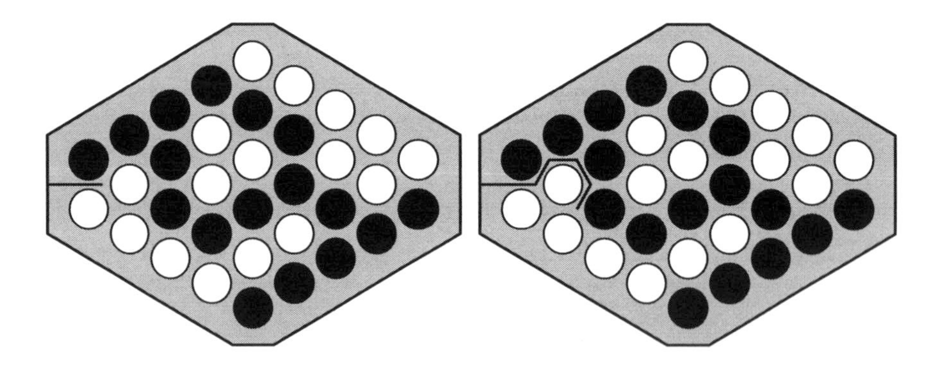

Figure 4.2. Continue the path: at each turn, keep a B-stone on its left and a W-stone on its right.

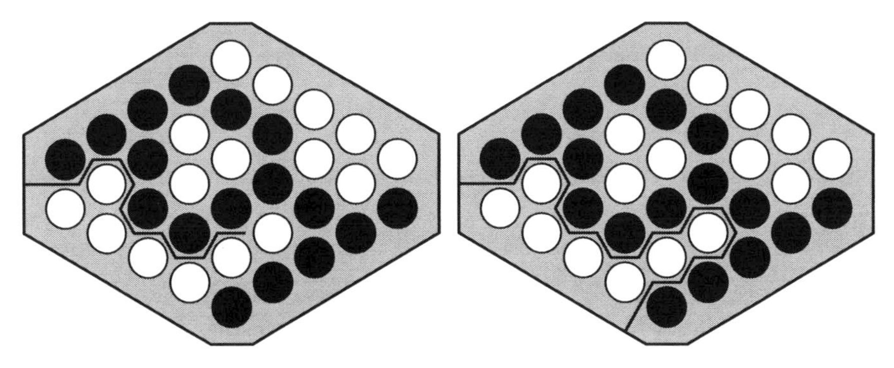

Figure 4.3. This path ends at bottom. On the path's left side a B-stone sequence joins B's edges.

segment, like those preceding it, has a B-stone on its left and a W-stone on its right. It also follows that, whenever a segment is added to the path by this procedure, the unchosen segment at this junction will *not* be added to the path in the future (that segment lies between two stones of the same color), and the new segment will *not* be later followed in the reverse direction (that reverse segment has the B- and W-stones on the wrong edges). Thus (3) the path can never revisit a prior junction.

Where can this path end? By (1) it cannot end at a 3-point junction, so it ends along the outside edge of the board. The path stays between stones of different color, so it ends between a B-stone and a W-stone. There are only four possible final locations: the four corners.

The path cannot end at the left corner: it started there and cannot double back on itself. The path cannot end at the right corner, which has a W-stone on the left and a B-stone on the right.

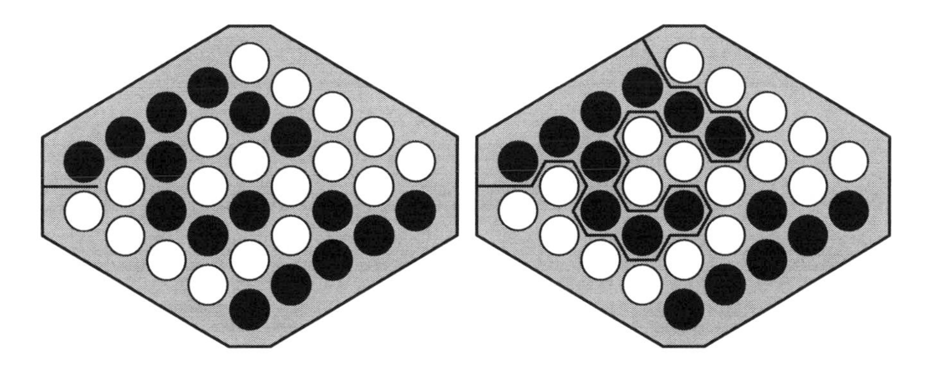

Figure 4.4. This path ends at top. On the path's right side a W-stone sequence joins W's edges.

Thus the path arrives either at the board's bottom, as in Figure 4.3, or at the board's top, as in Figure 4.4. In the former case, the B-stones on the left edge of the path join the two B-edges. In the latter case, the W-stones on the right edge of the path join the two W-edges.

This concludes Pierce's proof. Every filled Hex board has a stone set that joins one player's edges.

There is more to do to show that every filled Hex board has a path that joins the edges of *only one* player. This is showing that any two such paths must cross, and proving theorems about crossings in planar drawings is not easy! We will sketch a proof in the next chapter when we talk about Y. But Pierce's theorem is enough to prove that every game of Hex ends with a win. Can you see why?

In Hex, you move only if neither player has joined their edges. If your move joins your edges, you win and the game ends. If your move does not join your edges, then there is still no winner, so by Pierce's theorem the board is not full, so the game continues. But the board is finite, so the game eventually ends. Whoever makes the last move joins their edges, so they win.

4.2 extra stones

Here is the second property that we need for the first-player-wins proof. In a Hex game, suppose that you are White, it is Black's turn, and the position is as shown in the left of Figure 4.5. Your winning strategy is shown in Figure 4.6. In the right diagram of Figure 4.5, as a joke, a spectator puts a white stone in an empty cell. For this new position, it is still Black's turn. Do you have a winning strategy? Yes!

This might seem obvious, but it takes some care to prove. (It's not always true in other games. In chess, an extra piece — say a pawn — might interfere with needed mobility of some other piece, say a queen. In Go, an extra stone might remove a crucial liberty.) In Hex, an extra stone for you never hurts.

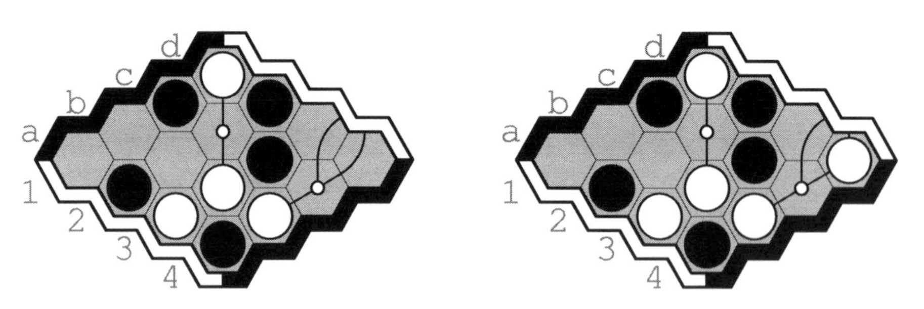

Figure 4.5. Black to move. (left) White wins. (right) An extra white stone, White still wins.

Why is this true? For a player — say X — and a starting position P, a *strategy* is a rule that describes, for any possible sequence of replying moves by X's opponent Y, what move X will make. We can describe a strategy for X with a dot-line diagram called a *game tree*.

In a game tree, each dot, or *node*, represents a position of the game. The start node is the *root*, in this case P. Each line, or *edge*, represents a move that takes one position to another. For every position Q with X to play, the corresponding tree node has exactly one child, associated with the strategy's unique X-move from Q. For every position R with Y to play, the associated tree node has one child for each empty cell in R, corresponding to all possible Y-moves from R.

Figure 4.6 shows the game tree for White's strategy in Figure 4.5. The root, corresponding to the starting position, has one child for each of Black's seven possible moves. The label on each edge shows the corresponding move. From each child of the root, the next move is that dicated by White's strategy. For example, after Black plays a1, White replies c2.

Why does the extra white stone in the right diagram of Figure 4.5 not ruin White's winning strategy? Because a winning strategy for the original position can be modifed to give a winning strategy for the new position. The only time White cannot follow the original strategy is when the required move is to a cell that already has a white stone! In that case, the goal of the original strategy — after the move, there should be a white stone at that cell — is already satisfied, so White can move to *any* empty cell, and carry on to win the game. In Hex, an extra stone for player X never wrecks an X-wins strategy.

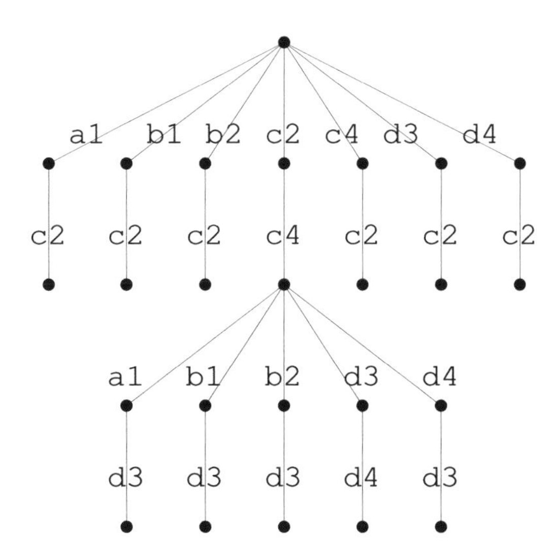

Figure 4.6. White's strategy for Figure 4.5.

4.3 strategy stealing

Now we can show you Nash's proof of the first-player-wins theorem: for Hex on any regular $n \times n$ board, the first player — say Black (B) — can win. Argue by contradiction: assume that B has no winning strategy. Hex has no draws, that implies that White (W) can win. B plays anywhere for her first move, say at cell x. W replies. Now what can Black do?

B can steal W's second-player-wins strategy! As in Figure 4.7, she considers the current position, B pretends that her cell at x is not there, interchanges colors and edges of the position, looks up the next move from W's strategy, changes colors and edges back again, and makes the corresponding move. B's stone at x is extra to this strategy, so W's modified strategy can occasionally ask her to move to a cell that she already occupies. As we have seen, B can moves to any empty cell, and B still wins.

Thus B — the first player, pretending to be the second player but with an extra stone — can follow what we assume is a second-player-wins strategy. But W *is* the second player, so W can also follow this second-player-wins strategy. B and W both win, impossible!

We have reached a contradiction, so our original assumption — there is a second-player-wins strategy — is false. There is no second-player-wins strategy! Hex has no draws, so there must be a first-player wins strategy. And that is the end of Nash's proof.

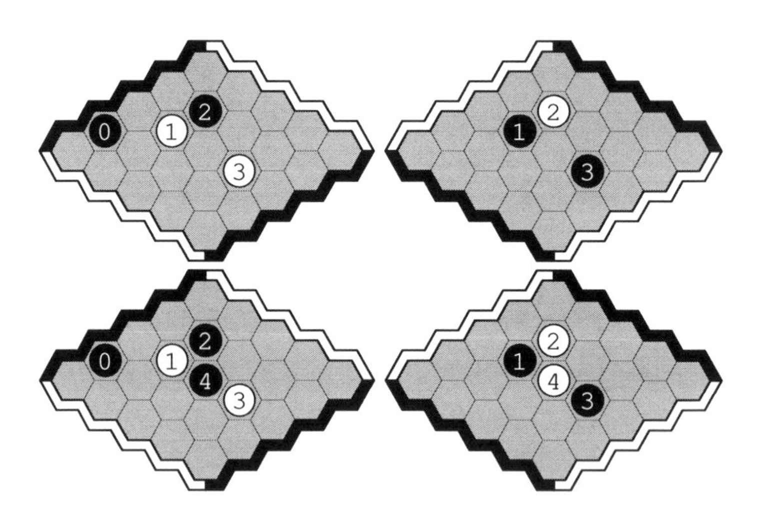

Figure 4.7. Strategy-stealing example. (top left, go clockwise) B forgets move 0, steals W's strategy, finds next W-move 4, makes her B-move 4.

4.4 irregular boards

Nash's first-player-wins-Hex proof holds only for *regular boards*, with the number of rows equal to the number of columns. Look back at the proof: where is this assumption used?

In a letter to Gardner in 1957, the mathematician John Milnor described an amusing strategy for Hex on any *irregular board*, namely with more rows than columns, or vice versa: the player whose edges are closer together can win — even as the second player — by pairing.

Here's a puzzle: find such a pairing for 5×6 Hex. Figure 4.8 gives one solution. Split the board into two triangles and pair each cell with its mirror reflection (through the short diagonal) in the other triangle.

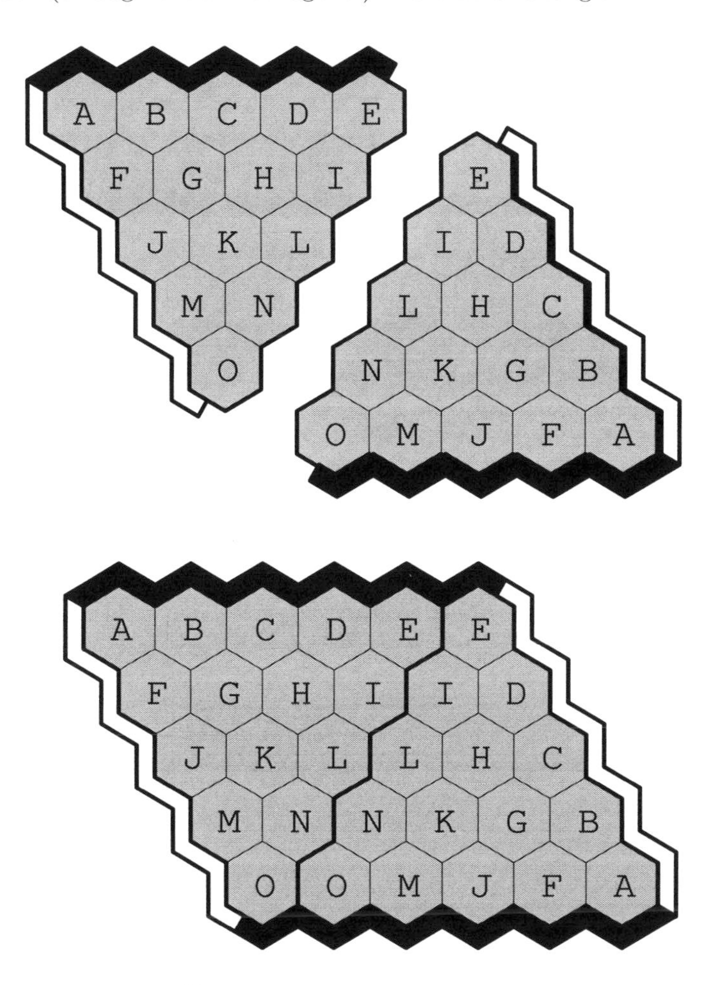

Figure 4.8. A 5×6 mirror pairing.

It's easy to follow this mirror strategy: Figure 4.9 shows a sample game. It's harder to prove that this strategy wins: can you do it? Spoiler alert: there is a proof on the next page. (What did that say? Did that say there is a *proof* on the next page? Do not turn the page!)

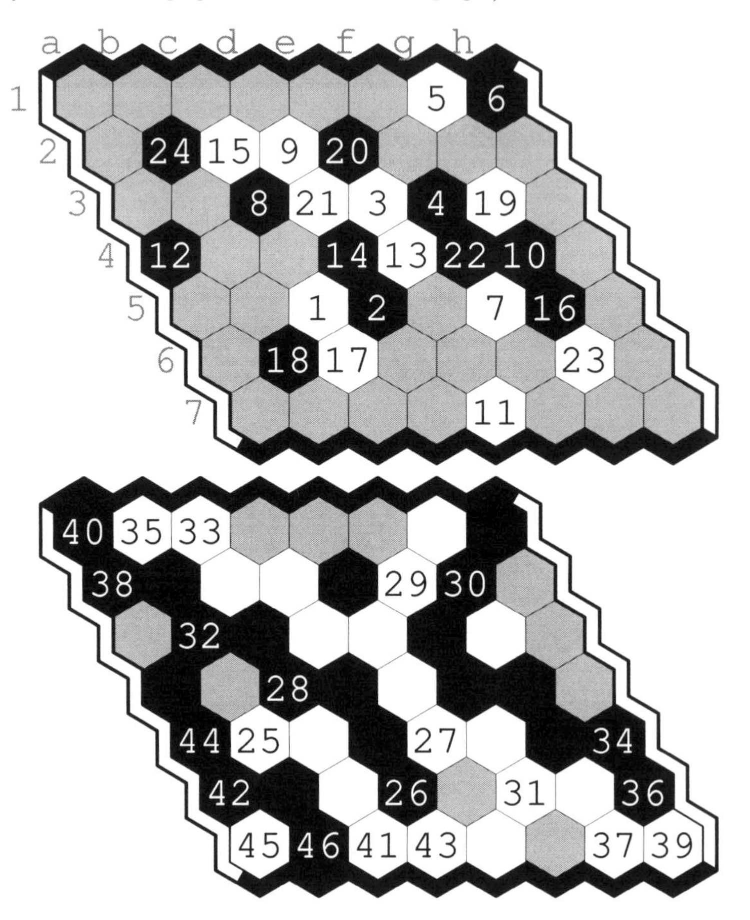

Figure 4.9. Black pairs White's moves and wins. Other moves might win more quickly, e.g. 24.B[e5] instead of 24.B[b2] or 28.B[f6] instead of 28.B[c4].

4.5 mirror strategy

Here is a proof that the second-player irregular-board mirror strategy wins. Assume that White (W) plays first, Black (B) plays second, B's edges are closer together than W's, and B follows the mirror strategy. See Figure 4.10. We claim that any path that joins W's two edges includes two cells that mirror each other. Thus the pairing strategy gives B a cell set that cuts every path that joins W's edges, so W never joins her two edges. Hex has no draws, so B wins. And that — after we have proved the claim — ends the proof: the irregular board mirror strategy wins!

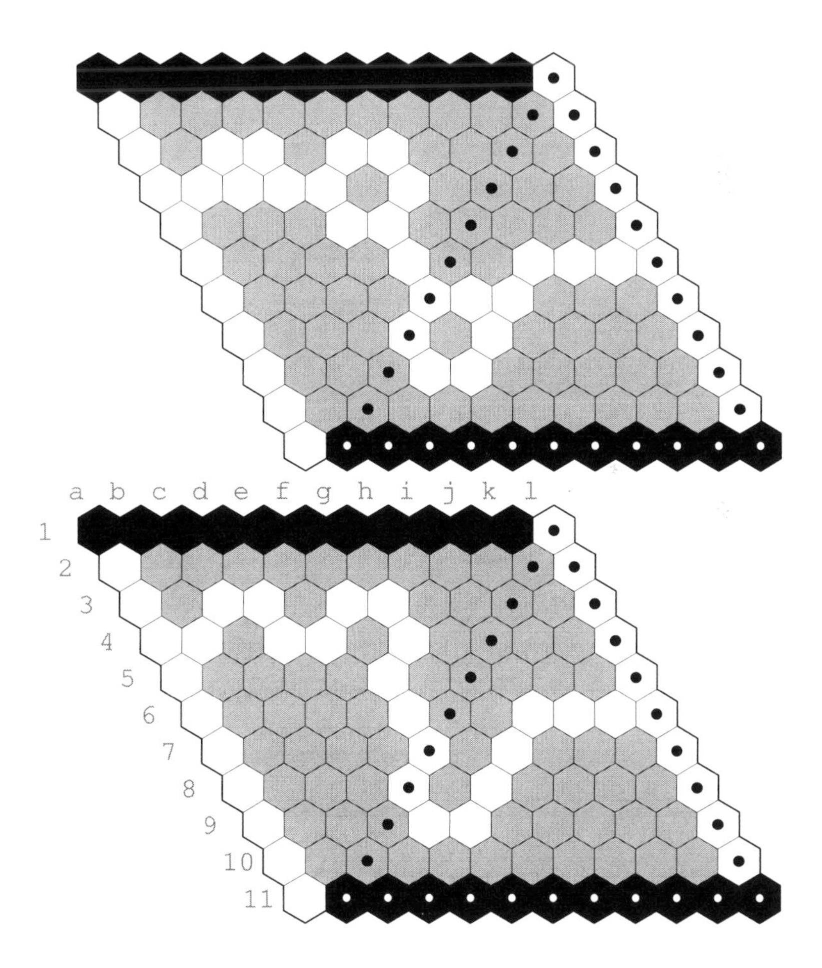

Figure 4.10. Dots outline the right triangle. (top) A W-path that joins W's edges. (bottom) This minimal W-path P still joins W's edges.

Now let's prove the claim. Start with any path that joins W's two edges. As long as this path has a cell whose removal leaves a W-edge-joining path, remove it. Label the resulting minimal path $P = (p_1, \ldots, p_j, \ldots, p_t)$ so that p_1 touches W's left edge, p_j is the first P-cell in the right-triangle half of the board, and p_t touches W's right edge. In Figure 4.10 these are b4, f7, k6 respectively.

Let $P_0 = (p_1, \ldots, p_{j-1})$ be the subpath of P from p_1 to p_{j-1}: in Figure 4.11, this is the white path from b4 to f6. Let Q_0 be the mirror of P_0: in Figure 4.11, this is the black path from i10 to g6. If p_j is in Q_0 then $\{p_{j-1}, p_j\}$ is a mirror pair and the claim is proved, so assume not. (In Figure 4.11, p_j is f7 and is not in the black path Q_0.) Then — as in Figure 4.11 — p_j (f7 in the figure, with the white dot) is below p_{j-1} (f6 in the figure): now the continuous boundary formed by P_0, Q_0, the left W-edge and the bottom B-edge separates p_j — with the white dot — from the right W-edge.

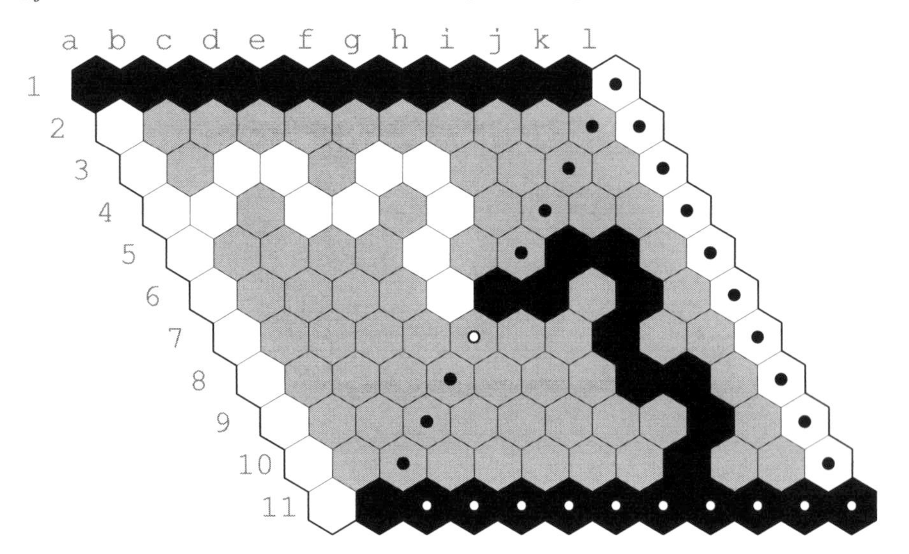

Figure 4.11. The left W-edge, the white path P_0, the black path Q_0 and the bottom B-edge separate the white dot p_j from the right W-edge.

Let $P_1 = (p_j, \ldots, p_t)$ be the subpath of P from p_j to p_t: in Figure 4.12, this is the white path from f7 to k6. P_1 joins p_j to the right W-edge. The right W-edge is outside the continuous boundary (call it a circle) formed by the W-edge, P_0, Q_0, and the B-edge. But p_j is inside this circle, so P_1 must break out of the circle by crossing P_0 or Q_0.

P is minimal so P_1 cannot cross P_0. Thus, as in Figure 4.12, P crosses Q_0, and where it crosses is a cell c in P_1 and Q_0: in the figure, this crossing point c is j6, the white cell with a black dot. Since c is in Q_0, its mirror d is in P_0, and $\{c, d\}$ is a mirror-pair with both cells in P. In the figure, this mirror-pair is $\{j6, f3\}$: both of these cells are in the path P that joins White's two edges. By this argument, we will find such a mirror pair in any such path P. That ends the proof of the claim.

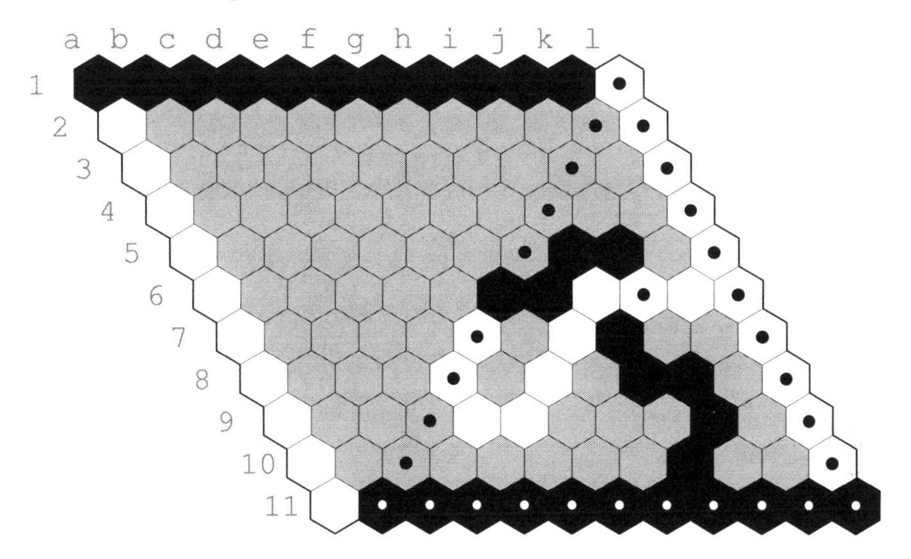

Figure 4.12. P_1 crosses Q_0 at the black dot.

4.6 puzzles

Here are some 5×5 puzzles with Black to play, each with one or two winning moves. How many winning moves can you find?

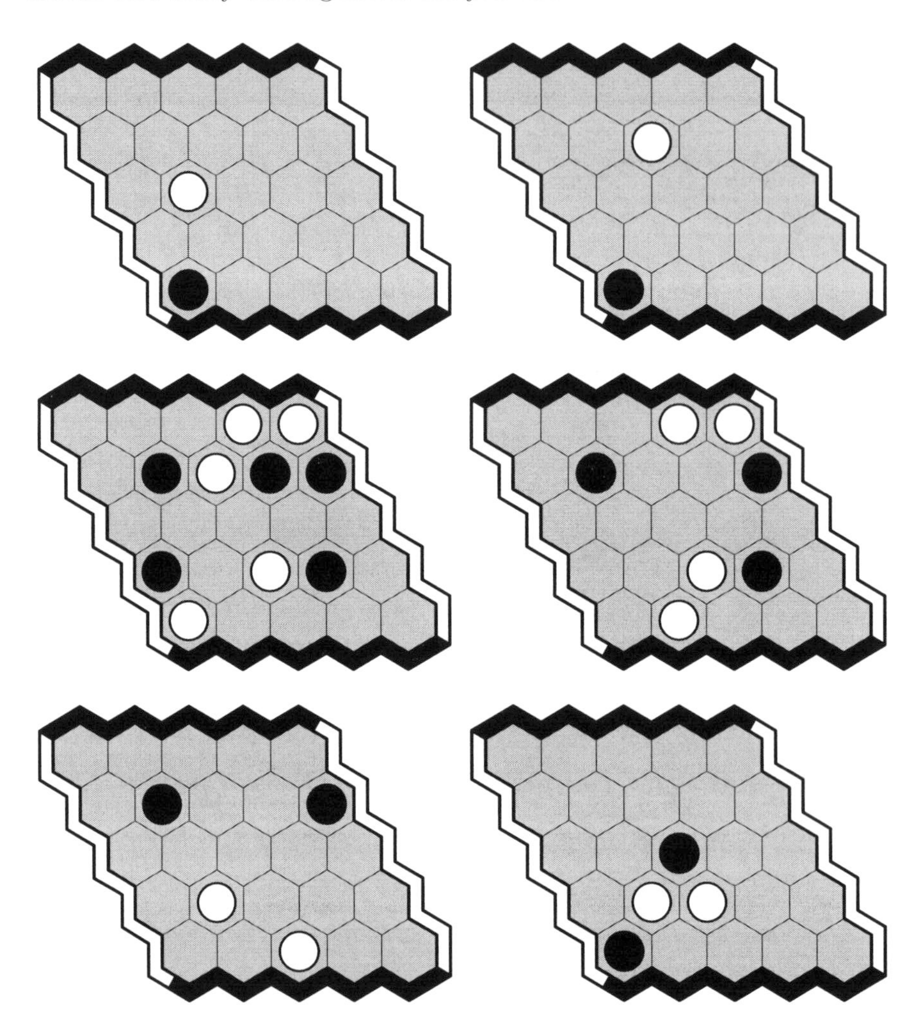

Figure 4.13. Black to play.

4.7 solutions

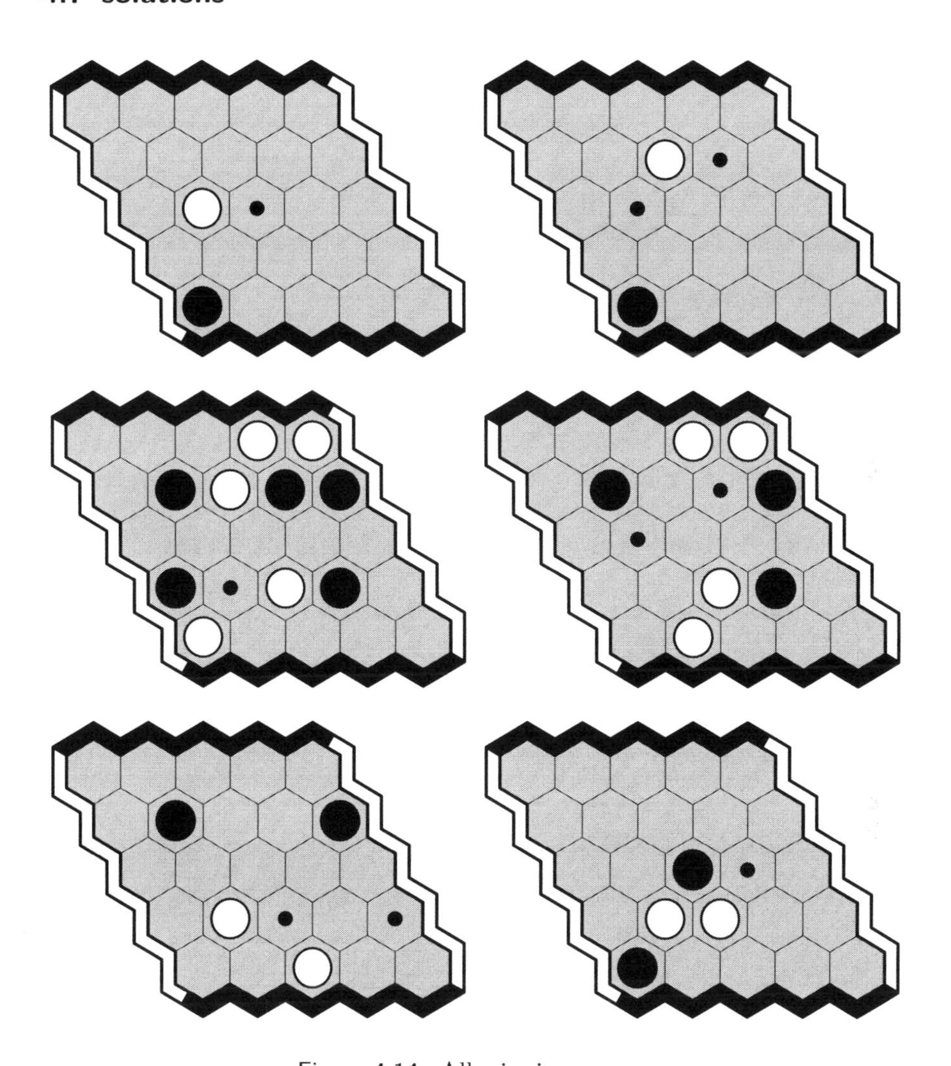

Figure 4.14. All winning moves.

5

don't go there

I try to read the game as well as I can.

Virgil van Dijk

Simplify, simplify.

Henry David Thoreau

In theory, playing Hex or chess or Go is easy: whenever it's your turn, make the move which — over all possible continuations of the game — gives you the best result. In practice, playing Hex or chess or Go is hard: on full-size boards, the number of game continuations is astronomically large.

What to do? In chess and Go, players have learned over centuries how to simplify the search for a good move by recognizing and rejecting some bad moves. In chess, when the king is threatened, ignore moves that don't save it. In Go, when a big fight starts, ignore moves that don't respond.

In Hex, some bad moves are easy to recognize. And — unlike with chess or Go — we can *prove* that they are bad. Let's see how.

5.1 minimal winsets

In Hex, a move helps you win only if it helps join your edges. For a Hex position and a particular player, a *winset* is a set of empty cells that — if given to the player — would join the player's edges. A winset is *minimal* if removing any of its cells wrecks the winset property. In Figure 5.1, removing a2 (or c2 or e3) from the top W-winset still leaves a W-winset: the top winset is not minimal. Removing e1 (or c2 or a5 or c4 or c5) from the top B-winset still leaves a B-winset, so the top B-winset is not minimal. Removing any cell from either bottom winset leaves a set that is no longer a winset, so these two winsets are minimal.

A minimal winset set does not have to be a smallest winset. In the bottom right diagram of Figure 5.1, {b3,b4,c4,c5} is a minimal winset even though other winsets — such as {b3,b4,b5} — are smaller.

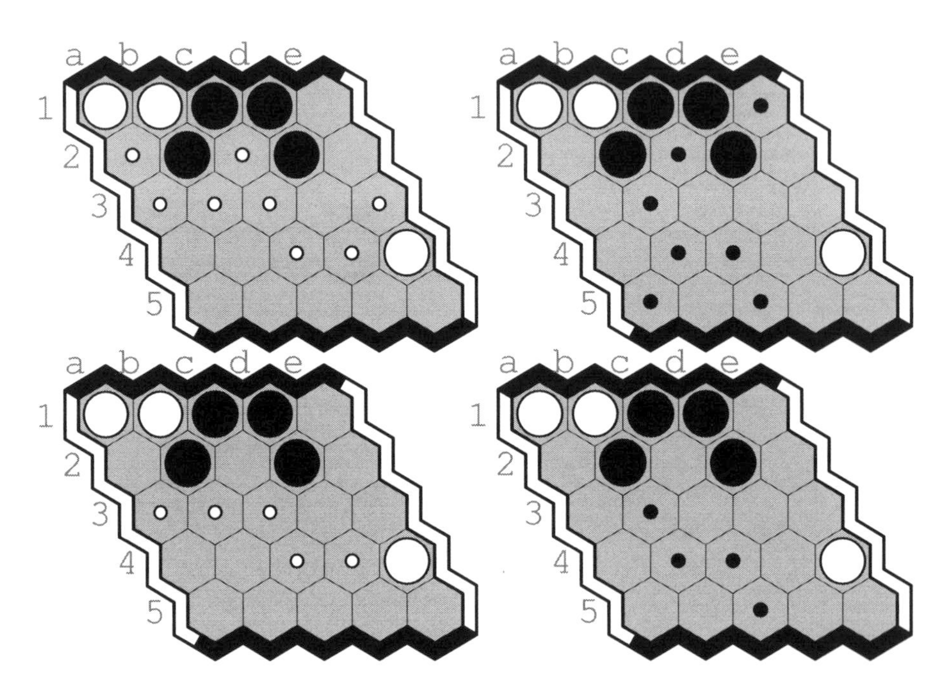

Figure 5.1. Only the bottom winsets are minimal.

We can use winsets to describe the Hex winning condition. For example, B wins 2×2 Hex by coloring all cells of any winset in Figure 5.2. We get a shorter description using only minimal winsets: B wins 2×2 Hex by coloring all cells of any of the three minimal winset in Figure 5.2.

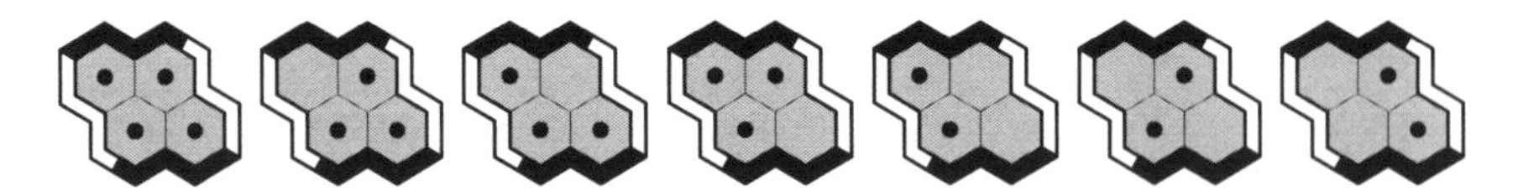

Figure 5.2. All winning B-winsets for the empty 2×2 board. The last three are minimal.

5.2 dead or alive

Here is the key observation: if you can win, then you can win with a strategy where each move is to a cell that is — at that moment — in some minimal winset. We call such cells *live* and all other empty cells *dead*. How many dead cells can you find in Figure 5.1? Figure 5.3 has the answer.

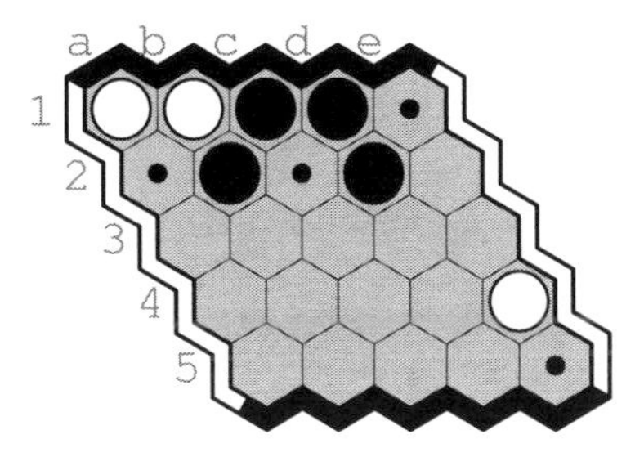

Figure 5.3. All dead cells.

It is easy to show that a cell is live: find a minimal winset that contains it. For example in Figure 5.3, {a3, a4, a5} is a minimal B-winset so these cells are live. It can be harder to show that a cell is dead: you need to show that *no* minimal winset contains it, and this might require that you find all minimal winsets. But sometimes you can tell that a cell is dead just by looking at its neighbors. For example in Figure 5.3, if cell c2 ends up in a minimal W-path that joins W's edges, then removing c2 must disconnect the path, thus the path must also include b3 and c3. But b3 and c3 are themselves neighbors, so this W-path does not need c2, contradiction. Thus c2 is not in any minimal W-winset.

In each pattern of Figure 5.4 the empty cell is dead. Can you see why? The preceding argument works for the first two patterns: we leave it to you to find arguments for the remaining three patterns. Using patterns, how many dead cells can you find in Figure 5.5? Answer in Figure 5.7. Hint: sometimes you can match a pattern by using a player's edge as a line of stones.

Figure 5.4. Each empty cell is dead.

To review: when it is your turn you can ignore any move to a dead cell. In fact, you can color it with either color: this will not change who wins. Also, you can ignore any move to a cell that can be *erased* — made dead — by a

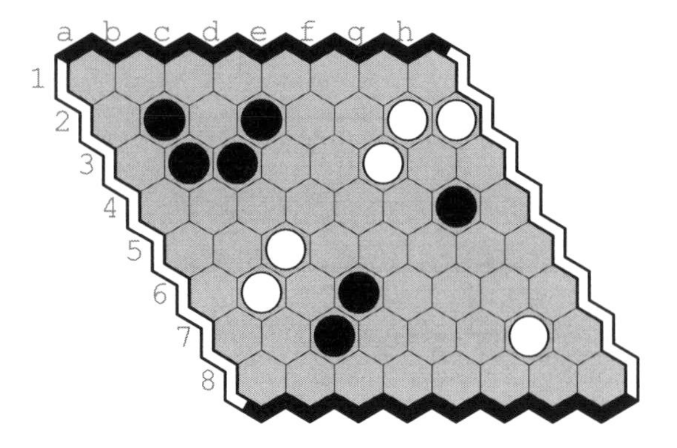

Figure 5.5. How many dead cells can you find?

move elsewhere. In Figure 5.3, a B-move to d3 erases e2, so a move by either player to e2 is inferior to a move to d3 instead. Each player can ignore any erasable move.

5.3 captured cells

We have one more trick to show you. In Figure 5.7, d1 is erased by a B-move to e1, and e1 is erased by a B-move to d1. Thus for the rest of the game, W need never play at d1 nor e1: if she does, B can reply at the other cell and erase W's move. We can B-color these two cells — which we call *B-captured* — without changing who will win! As with dead cells, some captured cell set patterns are easy to recognize. Figure 5.6 shows three such patterns. The dotted cells there are B-captured.

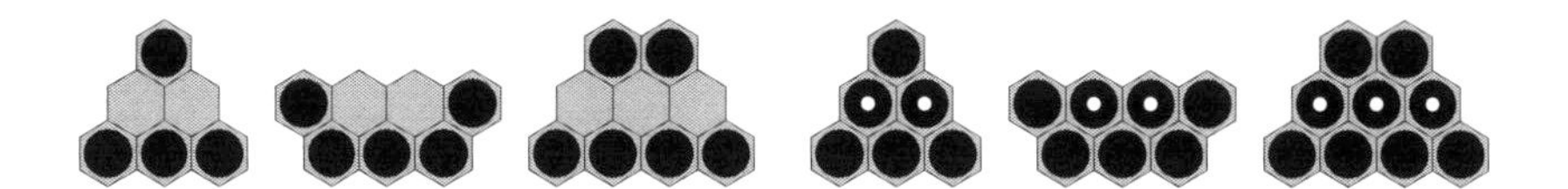

Figure 5.6. Filling captured sets. Here, each dotted cell is B-captured.

How many dead or captured cells can you find in Figure 5.5? After you find some, you can fill them in and keep looking. See Figures 5.7 and 5.8.

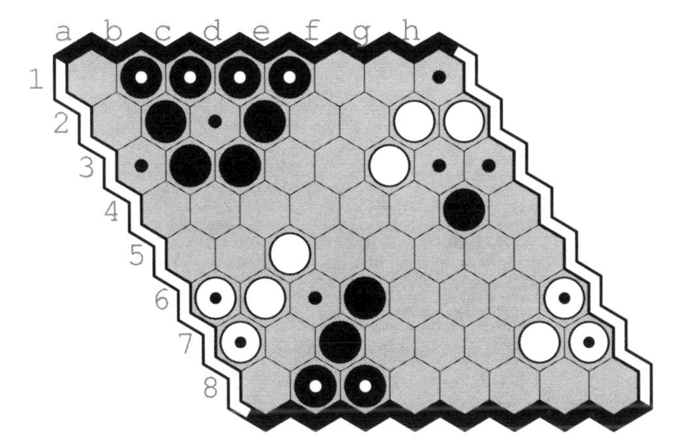

Figure 5.7. Dead cells (gray with a black dot), White-captured cells (white with a black dot), Black-captured cells (black with a white dot).

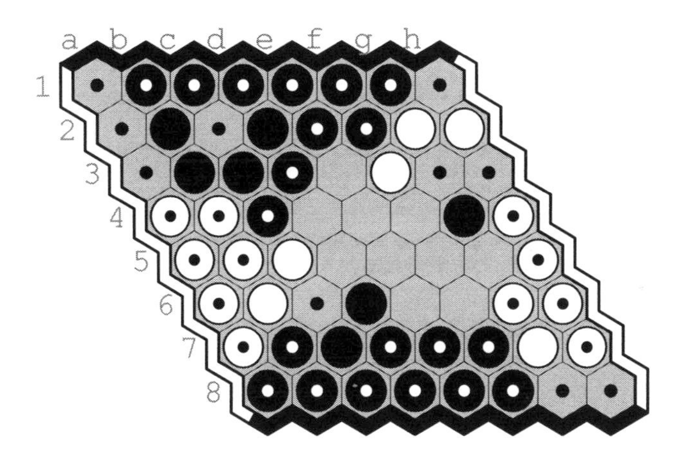

Figure 5.8. Continue to fill dead and captured.

Can you see how to get from Figure 5.5 to Figure 5.8? Using dead and captured patterns, fill the board as in Figure 5.7. Treat each dead cell as though it were B-colored: the particular color does not matter. Repeatedly apply dead and captured patterns. For example, calling the left W-edge column z, we have B-cells b1, b2, a3 and a W-cell z2 so, by a dead-cell pattern, a2 is dead. Now B-color a2. We have B-cells a0, b0, b1, a2 so, by a dead cell pattern, a1 is dead. Continuing in this way, you can reach Figure 5.8.

When analyzing a Hex position, you can fill dead and captured cells and ignore erasable moves. Next, some puzzles. Then, back to our story: what do we know about winning Hex strategies?

5.4 puzzles

Here are some 6×6 puzzles. The last puzzle has four winning moves, the others each have at most two. How many can you find?

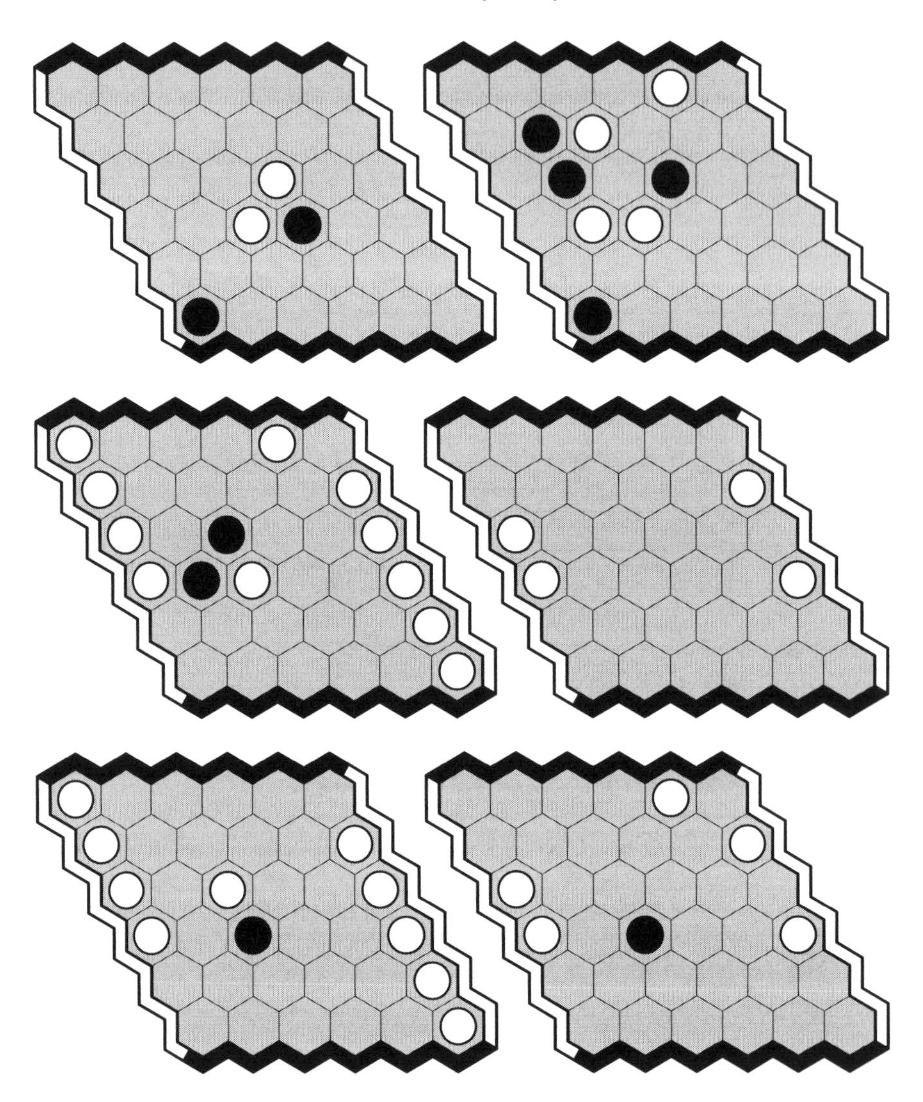

Figure 5.9. B to play.

5.5 solutions

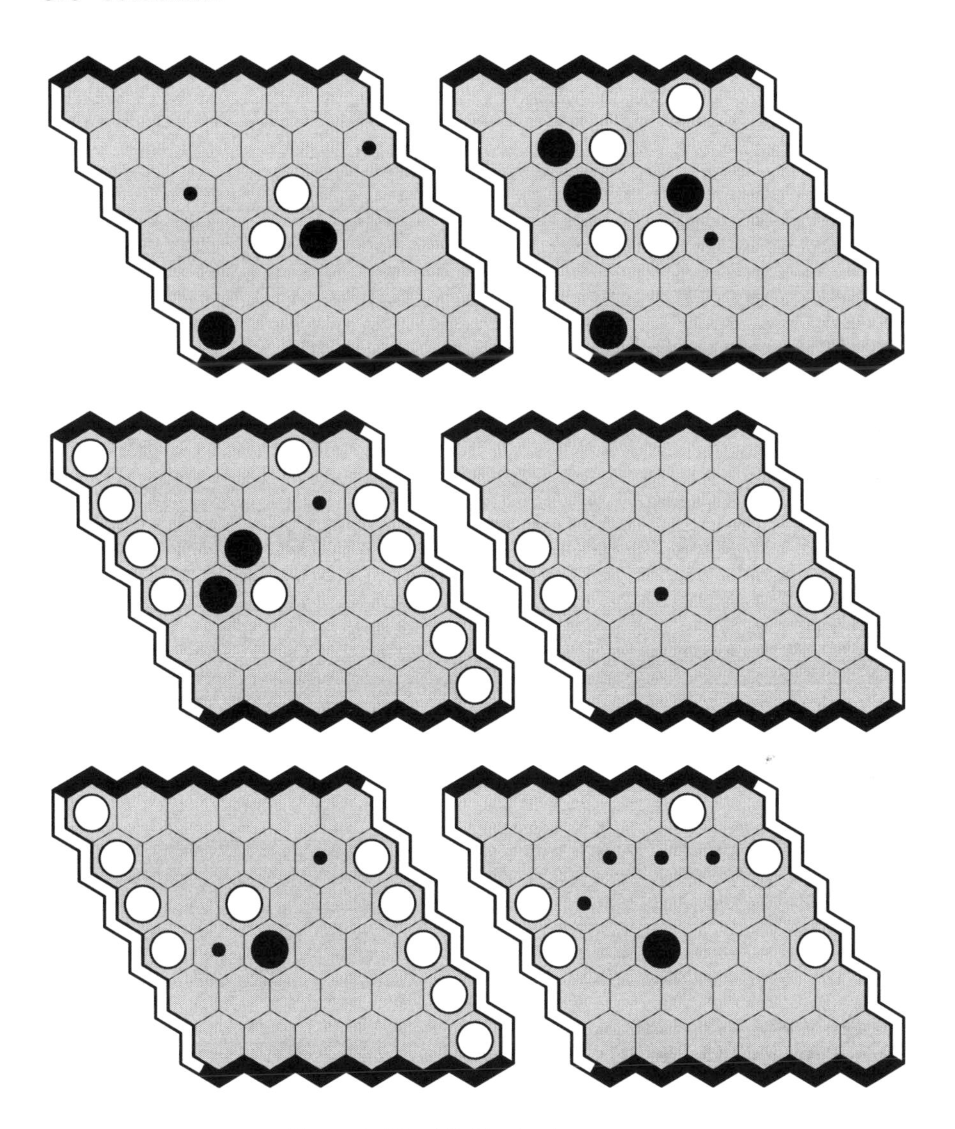

Figure 5.10. All B-winning moves.

6

back to Y

When you come to a fork in the road, take it.

Yogi Berra

Let's return to Y, also called Triangle. The rules are the same as for Hex, with these exceptions: a Y board has three edges; you win if a group of your stones touches all three edges. As in Hex, each corner cell touches two edges. The last diagram of Figure 6.1 shows a winning stone set shaped like the letter Y: that's how Y got its name.

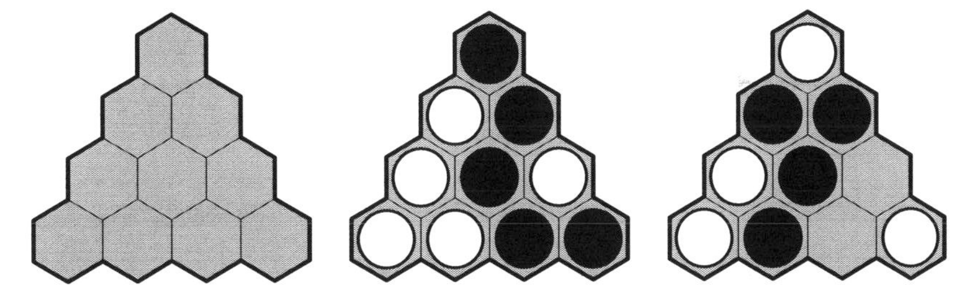

Figure 6.1. Empty board. Black wins. Black wins.

Try Y! Find a friend and play a game. The *base* of a Y board is the number of cells in its bottom row. For a base-4 board as in Figure 6.1, you will need (at most) $4 + 3 + 2 + 1 = 10$ stones to play a game. For the base-n board, you need $n + (n - 1) + \ldots + 1 = n(n + 1)/2$ stones.

6.1 warm-up

Let's warm up with three small Y puzzles. For each board in Figure 6.2, can you find all winning first moves? Solutions are below.

Figure 6.2. Find all winning first moves.

Solutions. Consider the base-2 board. Assume Black plays first. Cell A is a winning first move: it touches both left and right edges and safely joins the bottom with cell B or cell C. (This is the bridge virtual connection we saw earlier.) By rotational symmetry, B and C are also winning first moves.

Consider the base-3 board. By symmetry, there are two moves to try: a corner (say A) or a middle-edge (say E). A first move at E wins: it touches the bottom, safely joins the left edge with one of $\{B, D\}$, and safely joins the right edge with one of $\{C, F\}$. A first move at A loses to a reply at E.

Consider the base-4 board. By symmetry, there are three moves to try: a corner, the center, or a non-corner edge (say B). Opening in the center wins: bridge left, bridge right, bridge down. Opening in a corner loses to a reply in the center. Opening at a non-corner edge wins: to see why, work through the first page of puzzles at the end of this chapter.

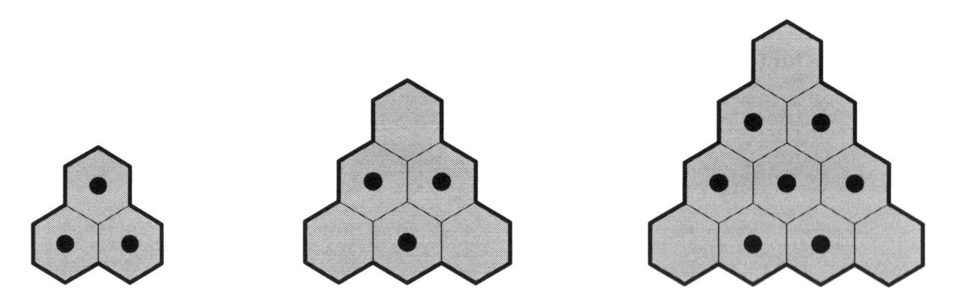

Figure 6.3. All winning first moves.

6.2 properties

Like Hex, Y has these properties:

- the game cannot end in a draw,

- the first player has a winning strategy.

In fact, Y generalizes Hex:

- put a Hex position P on a Y board, add black stones above and white stones at left: playing Y from here is the same as playing Hex from P.

For example, playing Y from the left position in Figure 6.4 is the same as playing 2×2 Hex; playing Y from the right position is the same as playing 3×3 Hex. On a base-$(2n-1)$ Y board you can play $n\times n$ Hex, so solving base-$(2n-1)$ Y puzzles is at least as hard as solving $n\times n$ Hex puzzles.

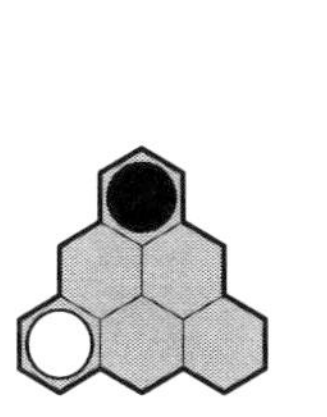
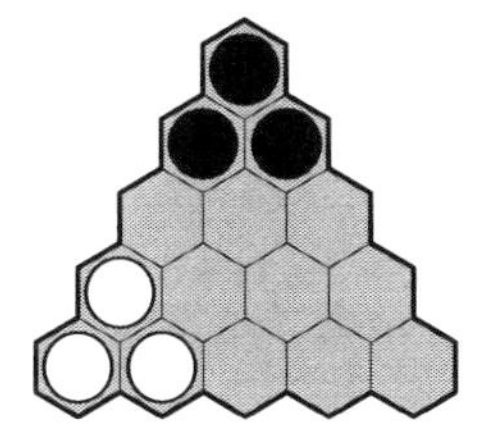

Figure 6.4. Playing Hex by playing Y.

Y was invented in Princeton by John Milnor [**18, 24**] and independently in Ann Arbor, Michigan by Charles Titus and Craige Schensted [**36**]. On large Y boards, the base length is more than three times the distance from the middle of a base to the center of the board. This makes moves near the center undesirably strong. But Schensted and Titus noticed this:

- the cells on a Y board can have different shapes: as long as at most three cells meet at a point, the game has no draws and the first player has a winning strategy.

They used this last property to dampen the importance of central cells, designing boards with central pentagons instead of hexagons. The boards in Figure 6.5 are based on Buckminster Fuller's geodesic domes.

Copy the boards and try them out! Or buy a copy of *Mudcrack-Y and Poly-Y* by Titus and Schensted from Kadon Games: it comes with hundreds of blank game boards. You can also buy a geodesic-Y board there: `http://www.gamepuzzles.com/`

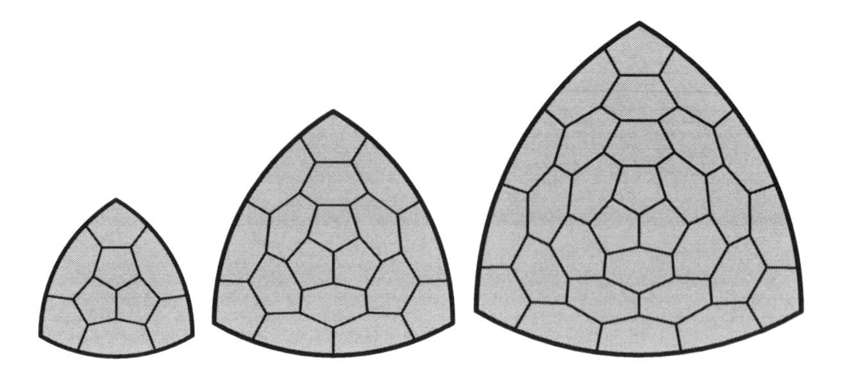

Figure 6.5. Geodesic-Y boards.

6.3 sample geodesic-Y game

Figure 6.6 shows a labelled geodesic-Y board and the start of a game. Black opens near the top with 1.B[k]. White replies 2.W[e], safely joining the right edge with a 4-3-2 connection {y,z,C,D,m,n,P,e,f}. After 3.B[j], White must play in {x,y,u,c,t,h,s,G,H} or Black can win with 5.B[s], so White tries 4.W[h]. Black replies 5.B[b] and White plays 6.W[q] to block Black from the bottom edge. 7.B[p] might have been stronger than 7.B[f]. With 8.W[p] the white group at {q,p} safely joins both bottom and right edges, using cells {C,D,E,F}. Black must stop this group from also joining the left edge, so plays 9.B[J]. White replies 10.W[u], threatening to join with with White's move 2 or 4. How can Black respond? Answer on the next page.

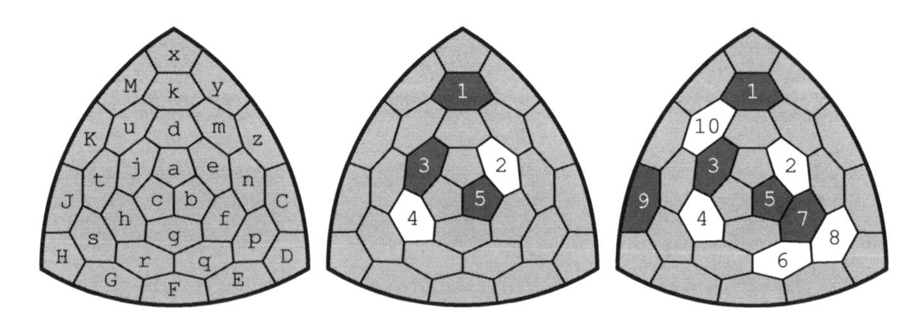

Figure 6.6. Start of a geodesic-Y game.

As shown in Figure 6.7, With 11.B Black attacks the white bridge joining moves 4 and 6. Rather than restore this connection, White pivots away with 12.W and the central white group safely joins 10.W via cells {t,d}. Can White extend this group to both the right and bottom edges? No: 13.B attacks this safe connection and is provably winning. White restores the connection with 14.W but 15.B splits White's moves 4 and 6. 16.W merges two white groups, but after 17.B the black group of moves {5,7,11,15,17} safely joins the bottom and right and can join the left on move 19 via cells {m,s}. With 23.B the black group {9,19,23,11,15,5,7,17,21} joins all three edges, so Black wins.

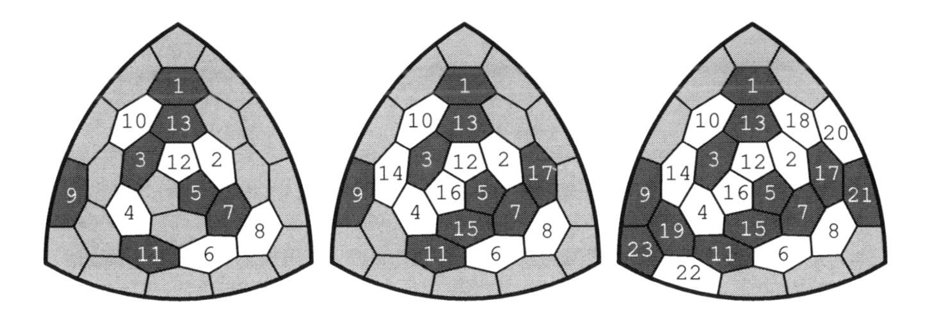

Figure 6.7. End of a geodesic-Y game.

6.4 exactly one winner

In an earlier chapter we promised a proof that a filled Hex board has a winning path for one — and only one! — player. Here we outline a proof by Craige Schensted of a stronger statement: a filled regular Y board (all cells are hexagons) has a set of stones that, for one — and only one! — player, touches all three edges [**22**].

Notice as in Figure 6.8 that The base-4 Y board has exactly six three-cell sets that each forms an upright triangle: in Figure 6.8 these are {A,B,C}, {B,D,E}, {C,E,F}, {D,G,H}, {E,H,I} and {F,I,J}. Also, as you can see in the figure, the internal intersection points of these three-cell sets correspond to the cells of a base-3 board. In similar fashion, for any base-n Y board there is a correspondence between the upright-triangle cell triples and the cells of the base-$n-1$ board.

Consider any filled Y board, say the base-6 board in Figure 6.9. (In the figure, White's stones are light gray.) The internal intersection point of each upright-triangle cell triple on the base-6 board corresponds to a cell on the base-5 board. Color each cell of the base-5 board using the majority of the colors from the three corresponding base-6 board cells. For example, in the

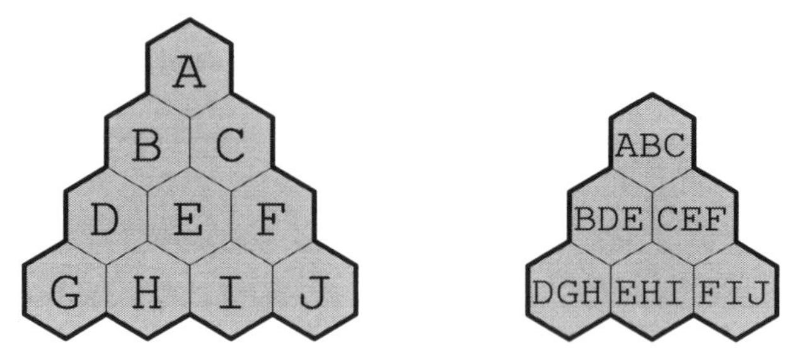

Figure 6.8. The upright-triangle cell triples of a base-4 board map to the cells of a base-3 board.

figure, the top triple of cells on the base-6 board has a white majority — two white stones, one black stone — so color the top base-5 board cell white. In similar fashion, reduce the base-5 board to a base-4 board, then to a base-3 board, then to a base-2 board, and finally to a base-1 board.

Here is a fun fact that we leave you to prove: a player has a set that touches all three edges on any one of these boards if and only if they have such a set on the following board. This ends our outline of Schensted's proof.

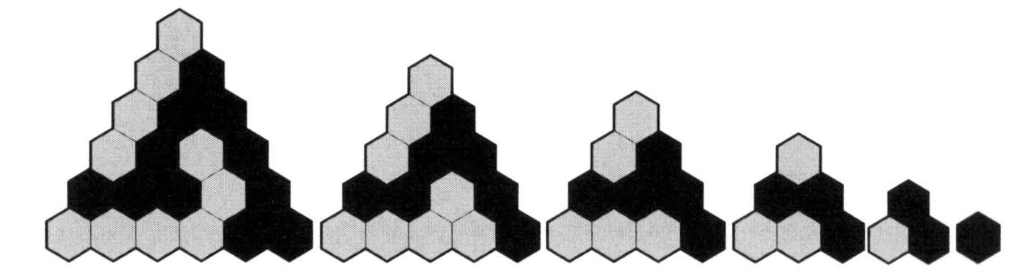

Figure 6.9. Schensted's Y-reduction.

Can a filled Hex board have a set of stones that wins for Black and a set of stones that wins for White? No. If such a position existed, you could extend it to a filled Y board as in Figure 6.4 and have a Y position with two winners, contradicting Schensted's proof above.

Schensted's theorem — every filled Y board has a winning set for exactly one player — holds for all Y boards, not just regular Y boards. But those boards can have irregular cell patterns and so require a different proof. We mention one such proof in the chapter on further reading.

6.5 draw a geodesic-Y board

Here's how to draw the 9-cell base-3 geodesic-Y board using a ruler and compass. To start, put a dot at the center of each of the six cells that form the spine of the board, at left in Figure 6.10. (The three lines are only to help you locate the centers.) Where do the last three dots go?

As in the next diagram of Figure 6.10, one dot is on a circle centred at the bottom right dot and including the other two outermost spinal dots and their midpoint. The next diagram shows the final dot placement. If you only want a simple board on which stones are placed on dots, add lines as in the last diagram and you are done.

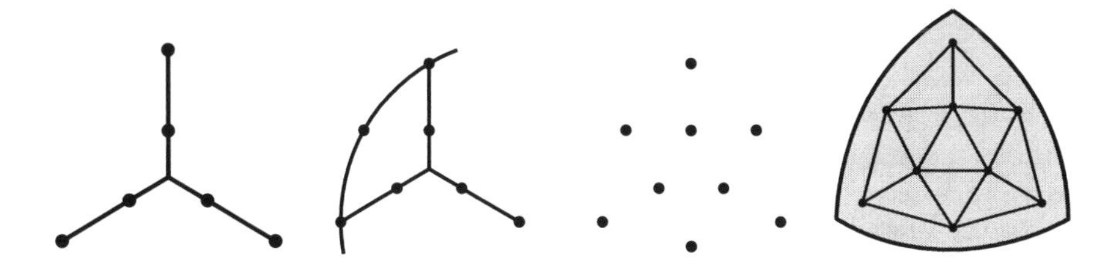

Figure 6.10. Draw a simple geodesic-Y board. On this board, place stones on dots.

If you want to draw the usual board — on which stones are placed in cells – use the cell centers to find each cell's perimeter. As in Figure 6.11, set the meeting point of three cells whose centers have x-y coordinates (a, b), (c, d), (e, f) to be $((a+c+e)/3$, $(b+d+f)/3)$. Then join these meeting points, and finally add cells edges to the outside of the board.

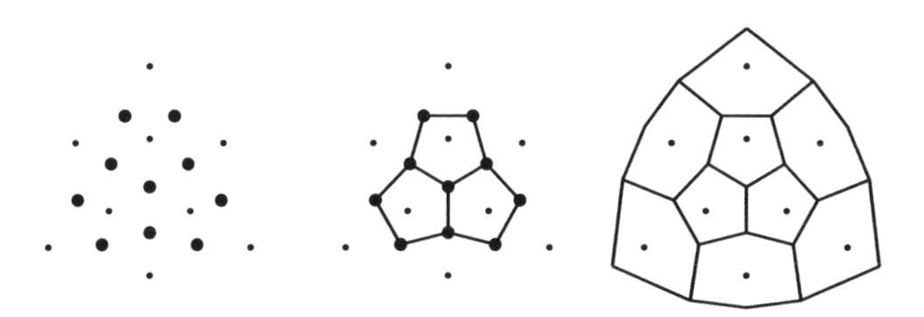

Figure 6.11. Draw the usual geodesic-Y board.

6.6 puzzles

Some Hex tips — virtual connections and must-play reasoning — also apply to Y. Other Hex tips apply, but not as often: in Y, neither player owns any board edge, so dead- and captured-cell patterns appear only rarely.

Enjoy these puzzles! Black to play: try to find all winning moves. Warning: the last three puzzles on this page are hard.

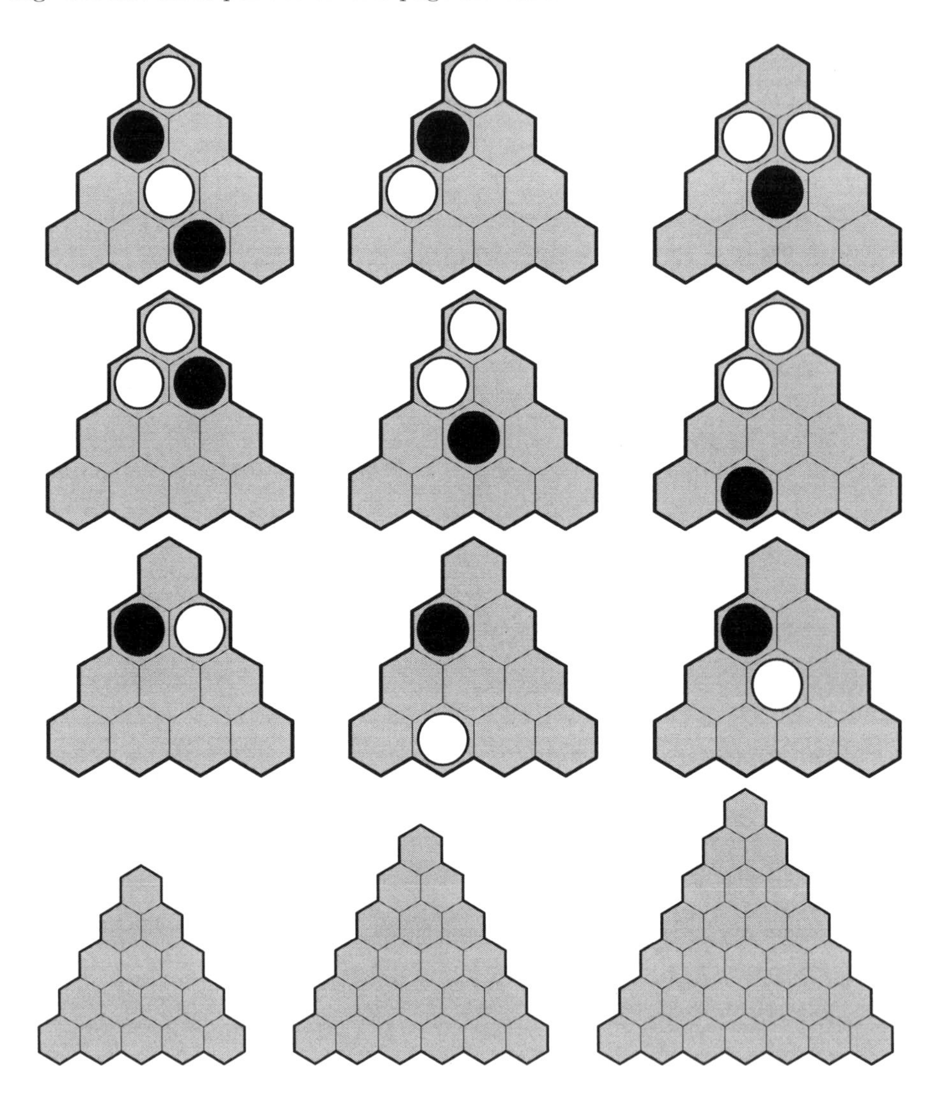

Figure 6.12. Black to play.

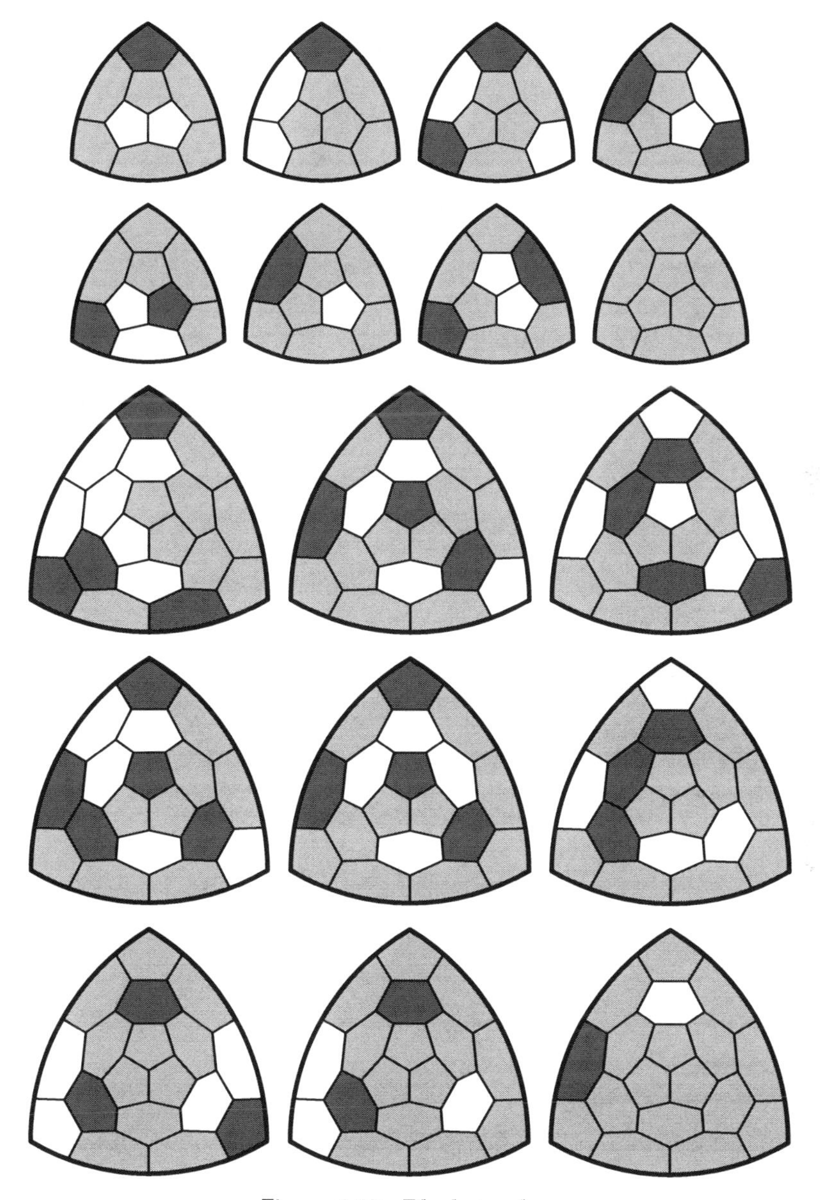

Figure 6.13. Black to play.

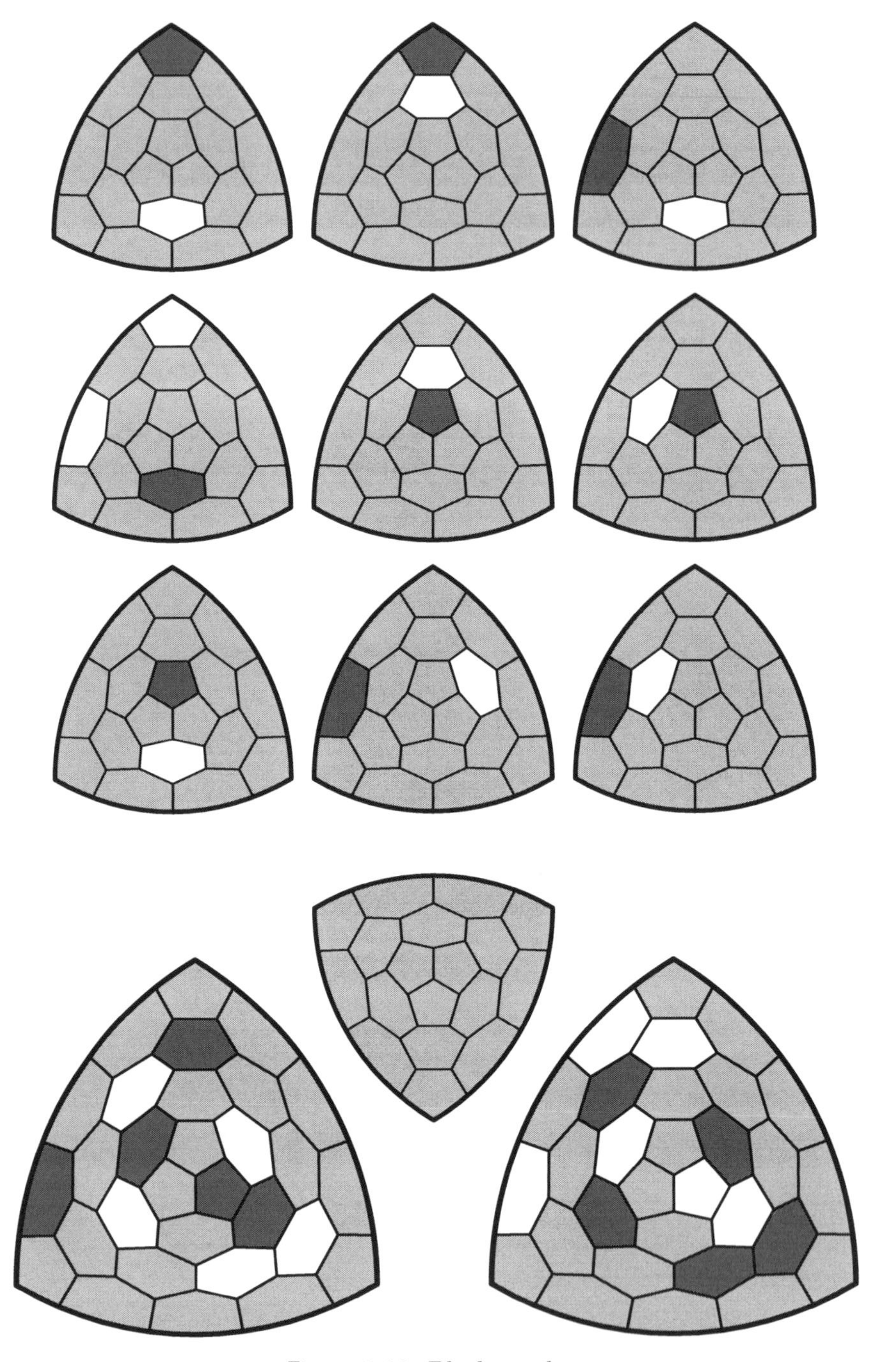

Figure 6.14. Black to play.

6.7 solutions

Bradley Hauer at UAlberta found the base-7 values by hand [**21**], mimicking the methods of Jing Yang for Hex [**42**]. Jacob Garber [**16**] and Timo Ewalds [**14**] at UAlberta wrote computer programs that can be used to check the other solutions.

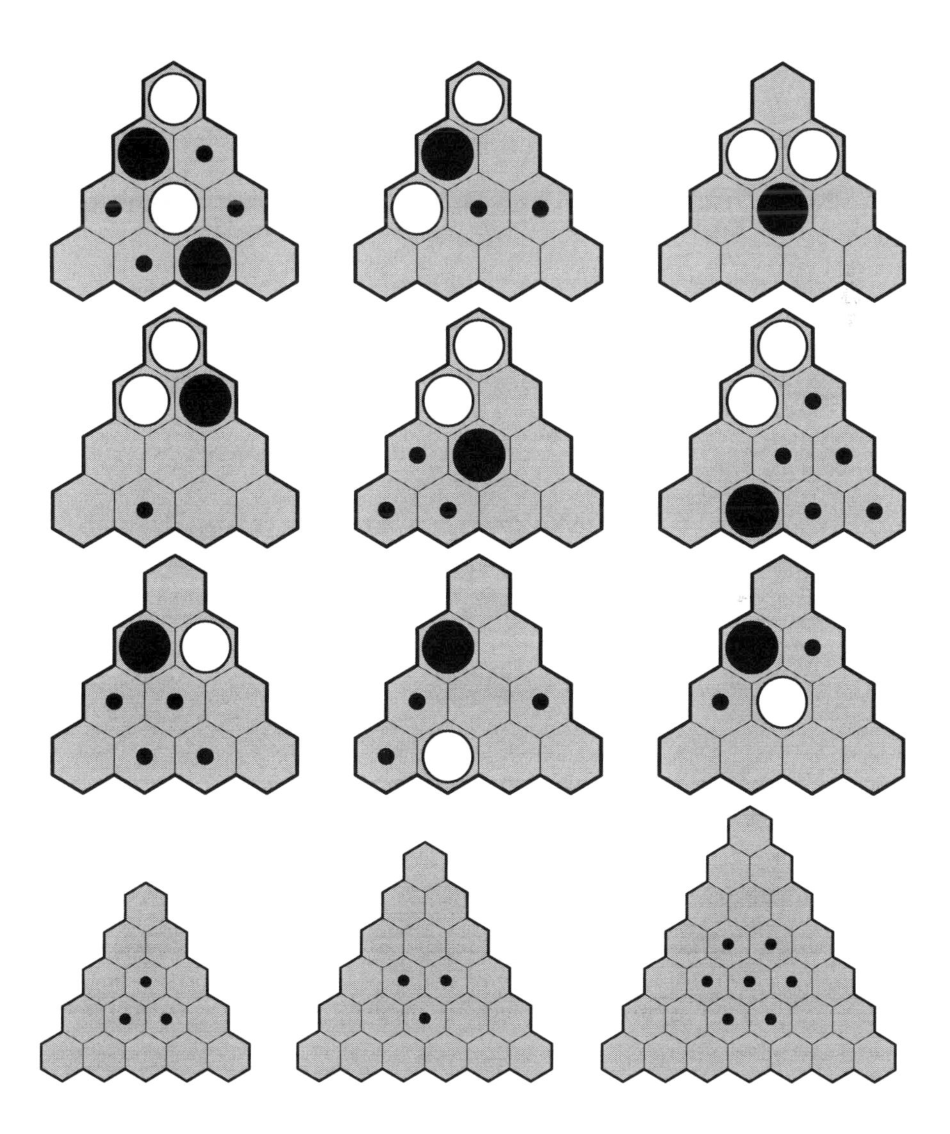

Figure 6.15. Black winning moves.

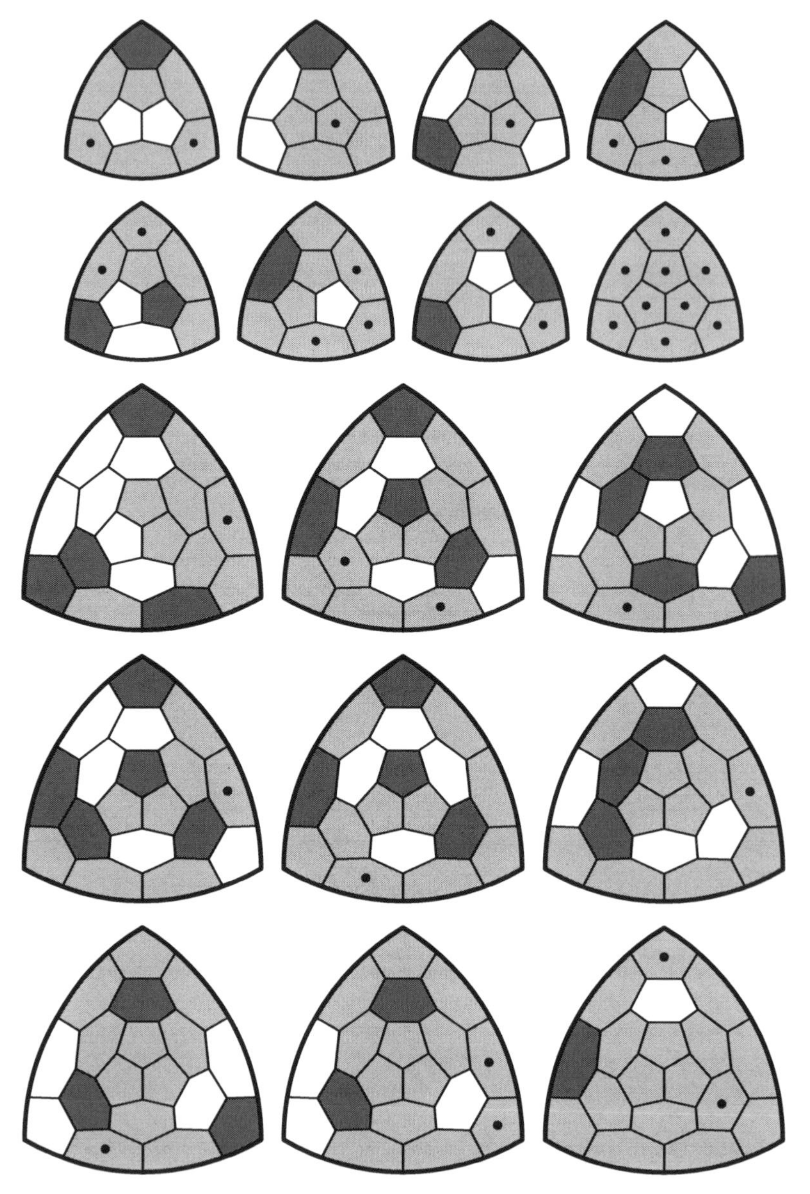

Figure 6.16. Black winning moves.

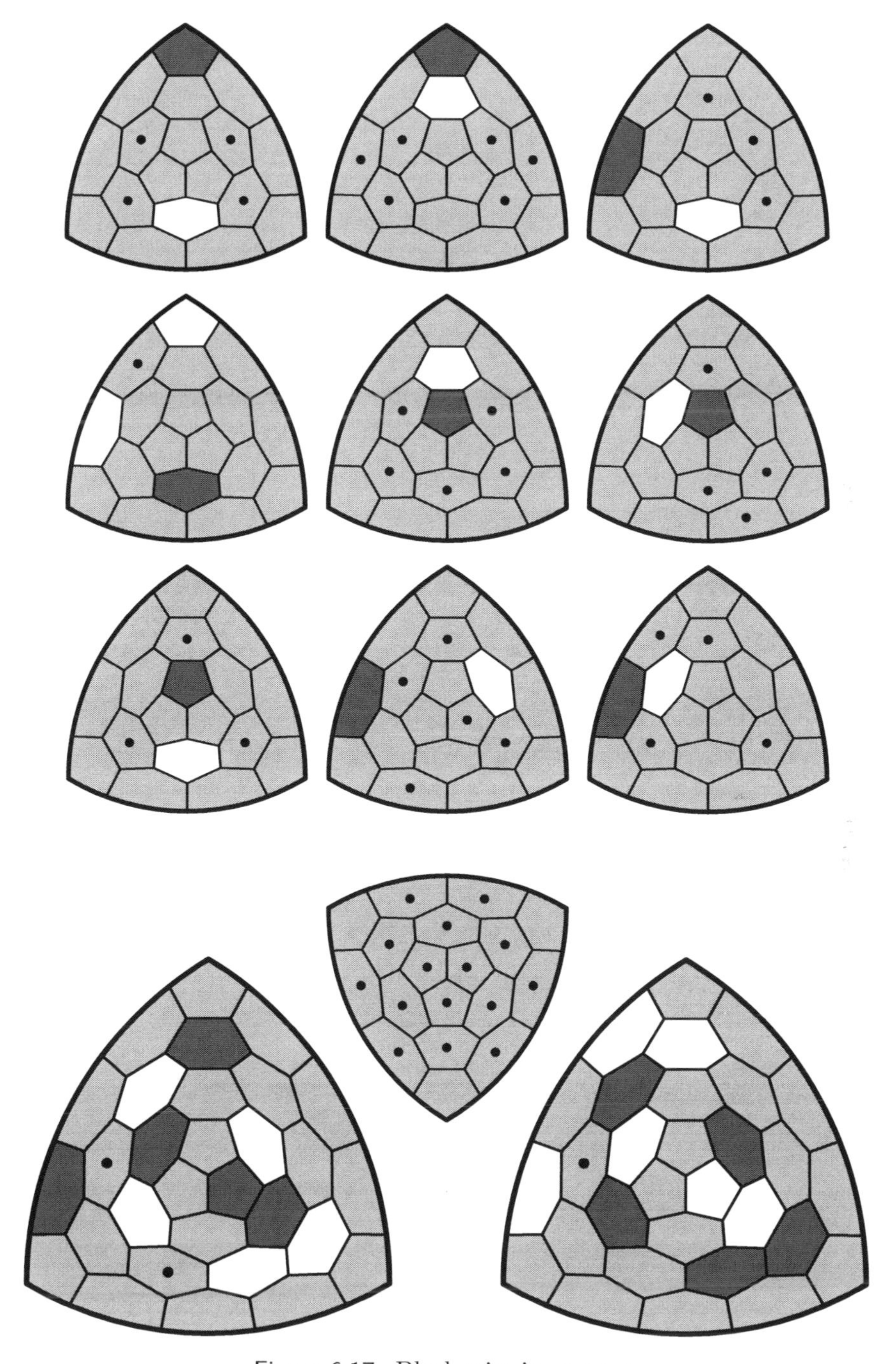

Figure 6.17. Black winning moves.

7

winning strategies

The board size and number of pieces make this game ingenious and difficult.
Gottfried Leibniz, writing about Go

Winning is not a secret that belongs to a very few ...
Gary Kasparov

Nash's amazing existence proof tells us that for any regular Hex board some first-player-wins strategy exists. But how hard is it to find such strategies?

Nash showed Gardner a first-player-wins strategy for each regular board up to 5×5. Can you find one for 6×6? It's non-trivial! Answer on the next page. Here's a simpler exercise: pick a winning first move in Figure 7.1 and find the rest of a winning strategy.

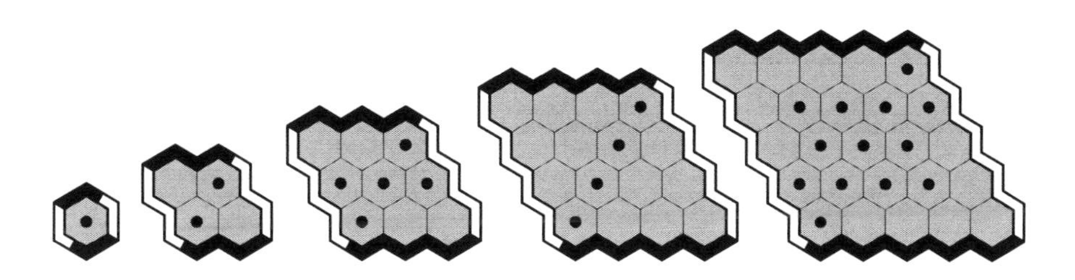

Figure 7.1. Each winning opening B-move.

7.1 6×6

At a Hex talk in Copenhagen in 1943, physics student Jens Lindhard explained the strategy shown in Figure 7.2. B opens in the center, labelled 1. W's 35 possible moves 2 are spread across the six diagrams. Each diagram shows B's move 3 reply to any of that diagram's move 2. For example, after any move 2 in Diagram A, B's move 3 safely joins bottom to top with two bridges and a 4-3-2 connection. B's strategies are straightforward in Diagrams B and C but trickier in Diagram D: how does B win there? Answer on the next page.

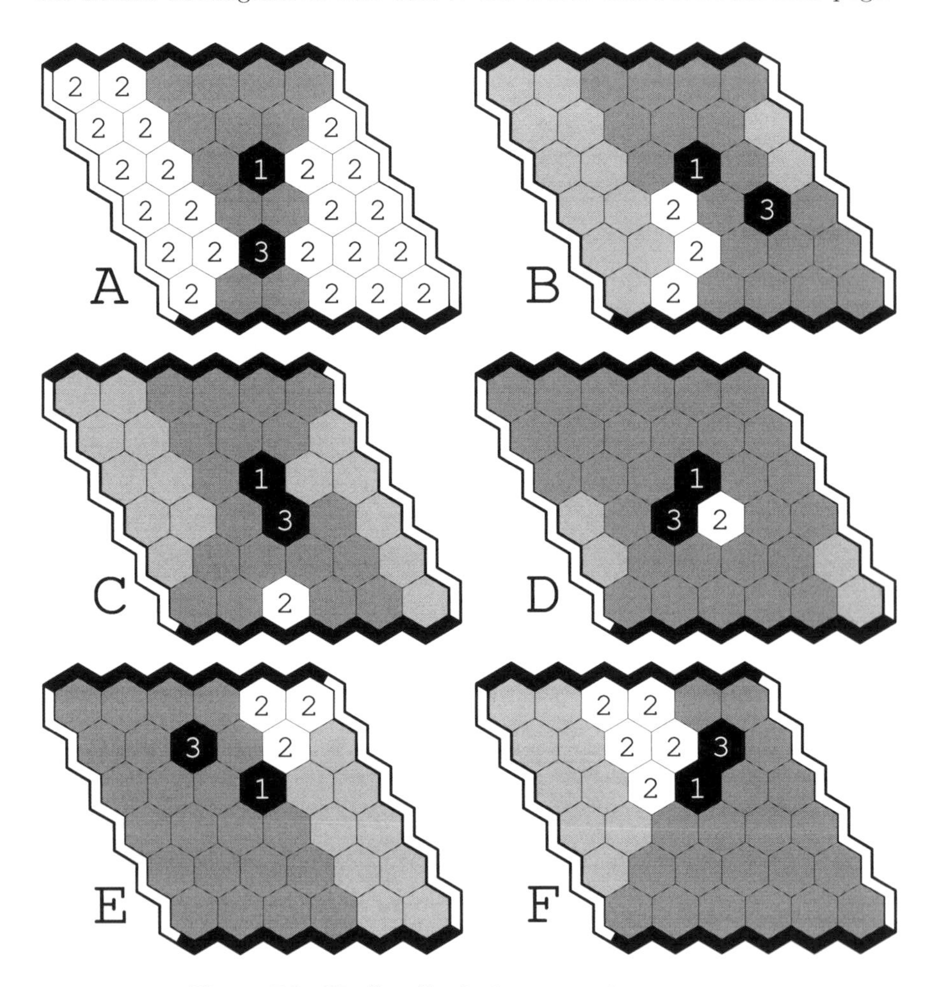

Figure 7.2. Lindhard's 6×6 center-wins strategy.
In each diagram, only the dark cells are used.

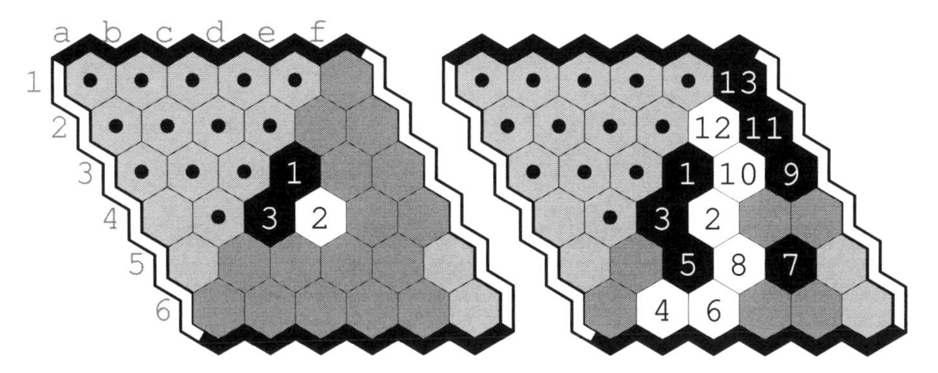

Figure 7.3. Join {1,3} to top with dots, and join {1,3} to bottom – or win – with shaded cells.

Figure 7.3 shows B's strategy for Diagram D. If W plays one of the dotted cells, B safely joins the 1,3 group to the top with d2 or b3. With the shaded cells, B starts at the bottom and tries to join the top directly. If W allows this direct attack then B wins. But if W blocks this attack then — shown in the right diagram — her moves are forced, and B can join the bottom to the 1,3 group, which can join the top with the dotted cells. B wins in each case.

Can you find a B-wins strategies for Diagrams E and F? In each case, B joins cell 3 to the top with a bridge. In Diagram E, B either joins 1 to the bottom or takes b5 and joins that to the top, either directly or through cell 3. In Diagram F, B joins the 1,3 group to the bottom.

7.2 7×7

No one has yet found an easy-to-describe strategy that wins on all regular boards: all we have are particular winning strategies for smaller boards. As you can see, these strategies get complicated as the board size grows.

Several people found winning 7×7 strategies, including computer programmer and Go expert Jing Yang. The six diagrams of Figure 7.4 illustrate a variation of his rotationally symmetric strategy. (Each diagram should be rotated 180 degrees to give an accompanying diagram. For example, if W's move 2 is to the bottom acute corner, then rotate diagram A to find B's move 3 response.) We leave it to you to work out how B plays in each diagram after move 3 — or you can read Yang's description of his strategy, which is 16 pages long!

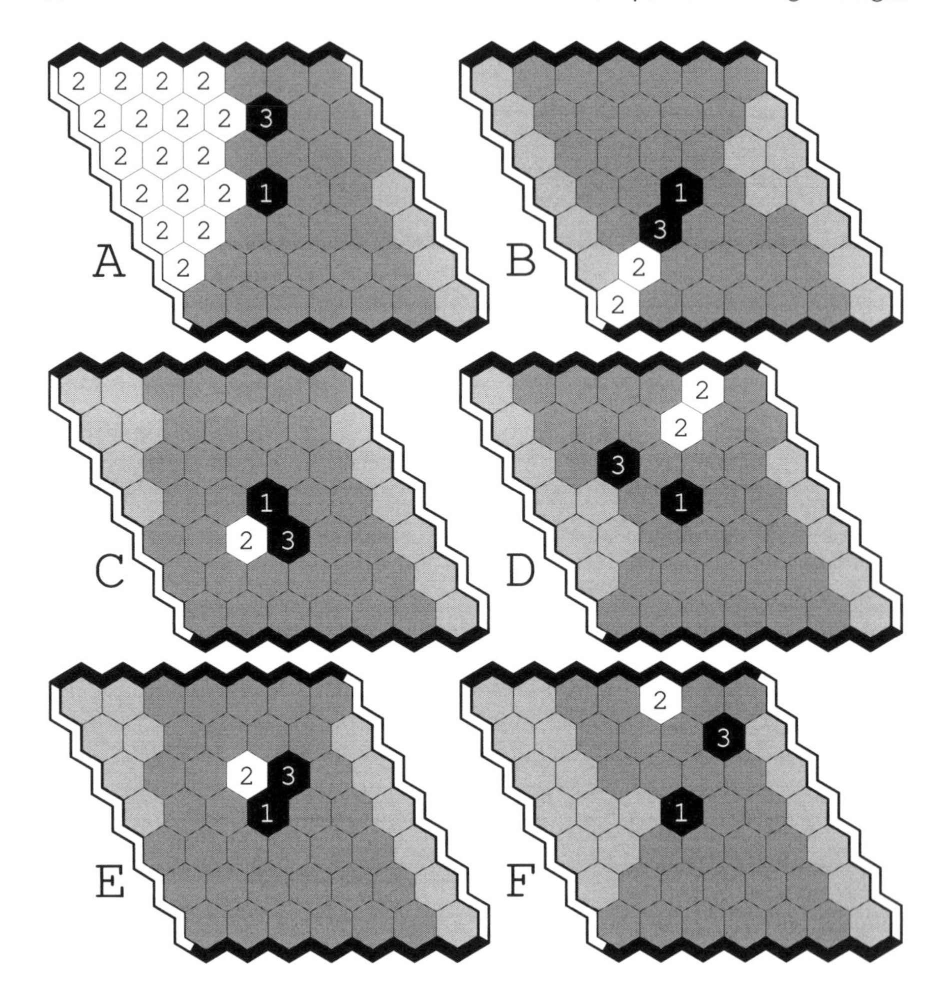

Figure 7.4. Yang's 7×7 center-wins strategy.

7.3 9×9

Yang also found 8×8 and 9×9 strategies. Figure 7.5 shows the first three moves of the 9×9 strategy. You can play against the whole strategy at the link below, on a visualizer written by David Pankratz. How many moves can you force the strategy to play before it finally wins?

`http://webdocs.cs.ualberta.ca/~hayward/355/asn/hexviz/`

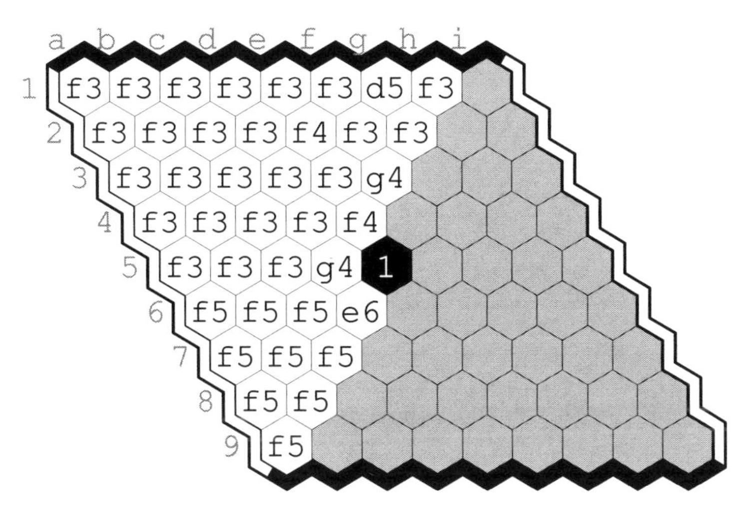

Figure 7.5. Start of Yang's 9×9 strategy, e.g. 3.B[f3] follows 2.W[a1]. The strategy is rotationally symmetric: a1 rotates to i9, f3 rotates to d7, so 3.B[d7] follows 2.W[i9].

Yang found his 9×9 strategy by hand. Using computers, Jakub Pawlewicz and a research group at the University of Alberta found two 10×10 strategies: we will say more in the next chapter. For $n \times n$ boards with $n \geq 11$, no explicit first-player-wins strategy is known. Maybe you can find one!

7.4 puzzles

Here are some 6×6 puzzles, this time with W to play. How many winning moves can you find?

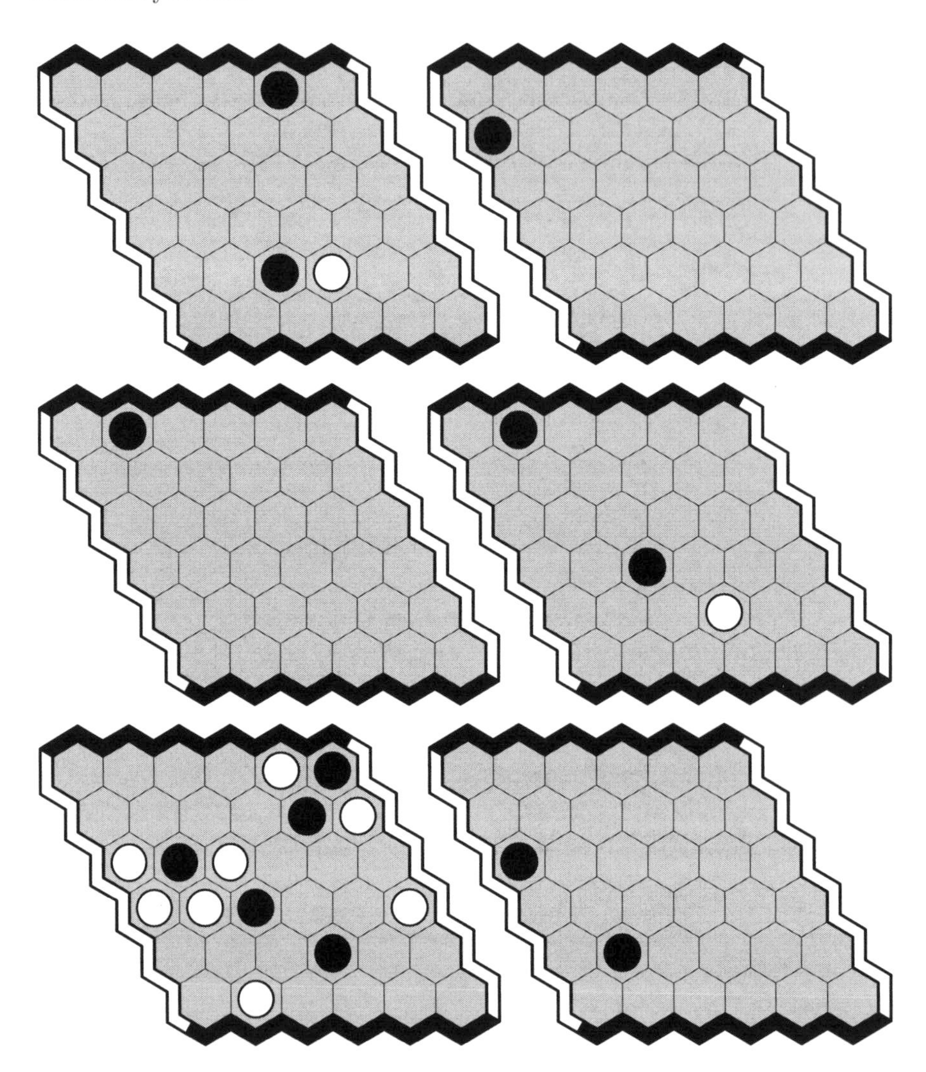

Figure 7.6. W to play.

7.5 solutions

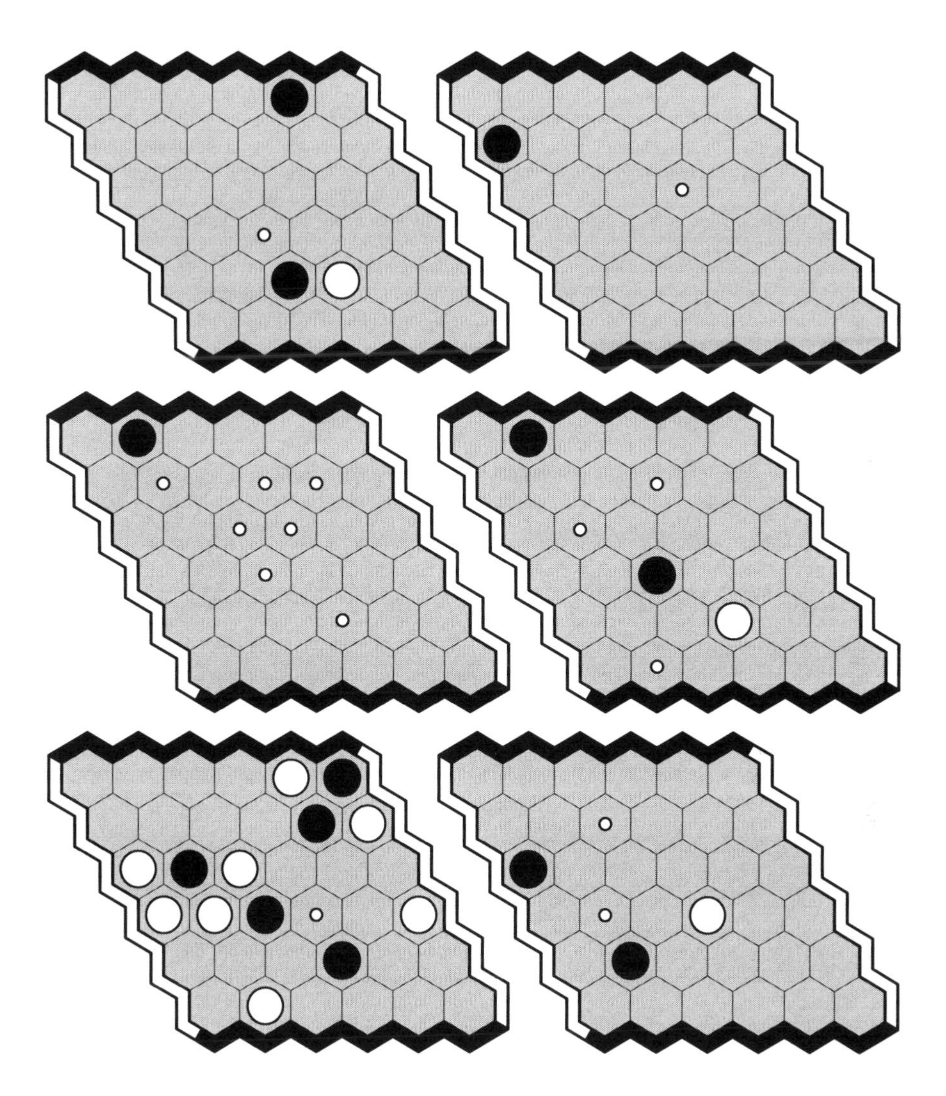

Figure 7.7. W to play.

8

computers

The Analytical Engine has no pretensions whatever to originate anything. It can do whatever we know how to order it to perform.

Ada Lovelace

Can computers find winning Hex strategies, or solve Hex puzzles, or play Hex? Yes, yes, and yes.

8.1 solvers

A simple way to solve a Hex puzzle is to consider all possible continuations of play and see who wins. (An algorithm that looks through the tree of continuations and figures this out, called minimax search, is easy to implement.) Ah, but there is a problem: the number of continuations can be too big.

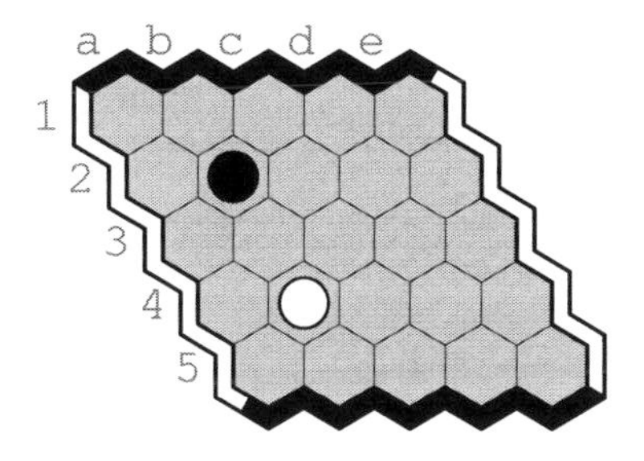

Figure 8.1. Black to play. Who wins?

Who wins the puzzle in Figure 8.1? Answer on the next page.

How would our simple method solve this puzzle? B (Black) has 23 possible moves. For each move, W (White) has 22 possible replies. For each reply, B has 21 possible next moves, and so on. For this puzzle there are 23! continuations. Actually, there will be fewer: many continuations yield a win before the board is full. If each continuation ends with the board half full, with 12 empty cells, then there will be 23!/(12!) continuations, less than 10^{14}. If your computer can analyze 10^9 continuations per second it will take less than 10^5 seconds — about a day — to consider them all, and then maybe the same amount of time to run the minimax algorithm and figure out who wins.

This sounds reasonable, but it won't work for larger boards. Solving a 2-stone 6×6 puzzle like this would take $34!/(18!\times10^9)$ seconds, which is more than 1,000,000 years! We have to reduce the size of the search tree. The good news is that we have already seen how to do this.

In Chapter 2 we saw that a winning move must block all win-threats. In Figure 8.1, W threatens to win with d3 and bridges {a4,a5}, {c3,c4}, {e2,e3}, so B must play one of these seven cells. With ideas like this, in the 1990s Bert Enderton at Carnegie Mellon University and then Jack van Rijswijck at the University of Alberta used a computer to solve 6×6 Hex openings.

In Chapter 5 we saw that captured cell sets can be filled. In Figure 8.1, {a4,a5} is W-captured and can be W-colored, so B's mustplay region shrinks to five cells. With this idea a new UAlberta group — Yngvi Björnsson, Michael Johanson, Morgan Kan, Nathan Po, and this author — solved all 7×7 1-move opening positions by 2003 [**23**]. See Figure 8.2.

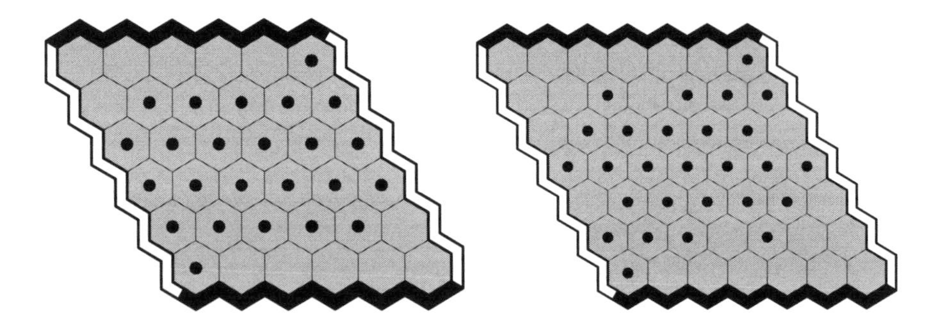

Figure 8.2. All 6×6 and 7×7 winning B-moves.

Joining the UAlberta group, Broderick Arneson and Philip Henderson solved all 8×8 openings [**1**] and Jakub Pawlewicz solved all 9×9 openings [**32**]. See Figure 8.3. Pawlewicz later found the only 10×10 winning opening moves known so far, the centermost cell and the second-row cell on the short diagonal.

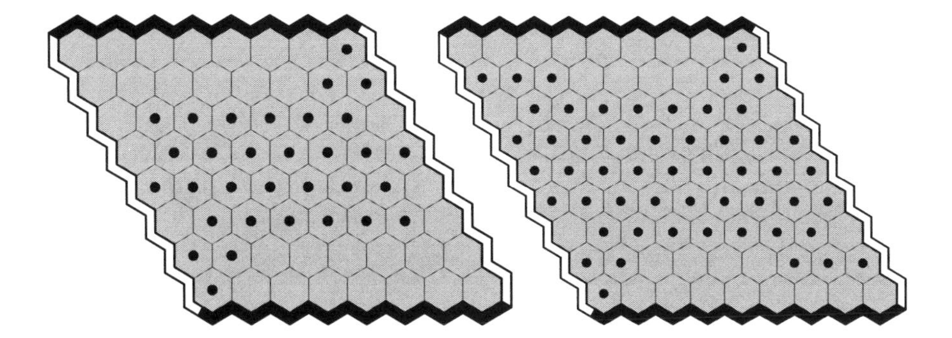

Figure 8.3. All 8×8 and 9×9 winning B-moves.

Who wins in Figure 8.1? B's mustplay region is {c3,c4,d3,e2,e3}: if B can win, then B can win by moving to one of these five cells. But c3 loses (W replies c4) and e3 loses (that's a puzzle at the end of the book). As shown in Figure 8.4, the other three moves win. For example, with d3 B safely joins the bottom and can also join the top: either e1 and bridge {d2,e2} or c3 and bridges {b3,c2} and {b1,c1}.

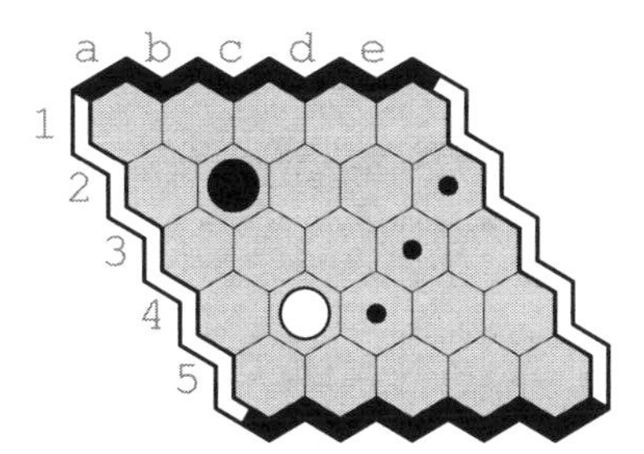

Figure 8.4. B to play. All winning B-moves.

8.2 players

Believe it or not, artificial Hex players pre-date programmable computers! In 1950 mathematician and engineer Claude Shannon and his colleague E.F. Moore, built an electric resistance network that could play 7×7 Hex. It made strong opening moves but blundered in tactical positions [**39**].

In the 1970s — 130 years after Charles Babbage designed his Analytical Engine and Ada Lovelace explained how to program it — programmable computers finally started to replace special-purpose machines. In the 2000s, as computer Hex solvers progressed, so did computer Hex players. By 2015 the strongest programs could beat most humans at a game of 11×11 Hex, but were still outclassed by humans on larger boards. And then ... boom!

In 2016 — just as DeepBlue had shocked the world nine years earlier by defeating chessmaster Gary Kasparov — AlphaGo came out of nowhere to upset the legendary Go professional Lee Sedol. Today's top computer players mimic AlphaGo and its successor AlphaZero, which learned to play superhuman-level Go and chess and shogi (Japanese chess) starting only from each game's ruleset!

Figure 8.5 shows a 2019 game between two UAlberta Hex programs, the pre-AlphaGo MoHex-2.0 (M2) and the post-AlphaGo MoHex-CNN (MCNN). M2, the result of a multi-year project involving more than a dozen people, does what you might expect: it computes virtual connections, fills dead and captured cells, and explores likely continuations using Monte Carlo tree search. MCNN, an AlphaGo-style successor to M2 designed and implemented by Chao Gao, integrates feedback from game-processing-units — trained using deep convolutional neural nets — into the tree search. MCNN did not have access to the crazy number of machines on which AlphaGo and AlphaZero trained so it is stronger than M2 but not yet superhuman.

What do you think of the game in Figure 8.5? For the first 19 moves, both players think they are winning. It is only after MCNN's move 20 that M2 sees that it is in trouble.

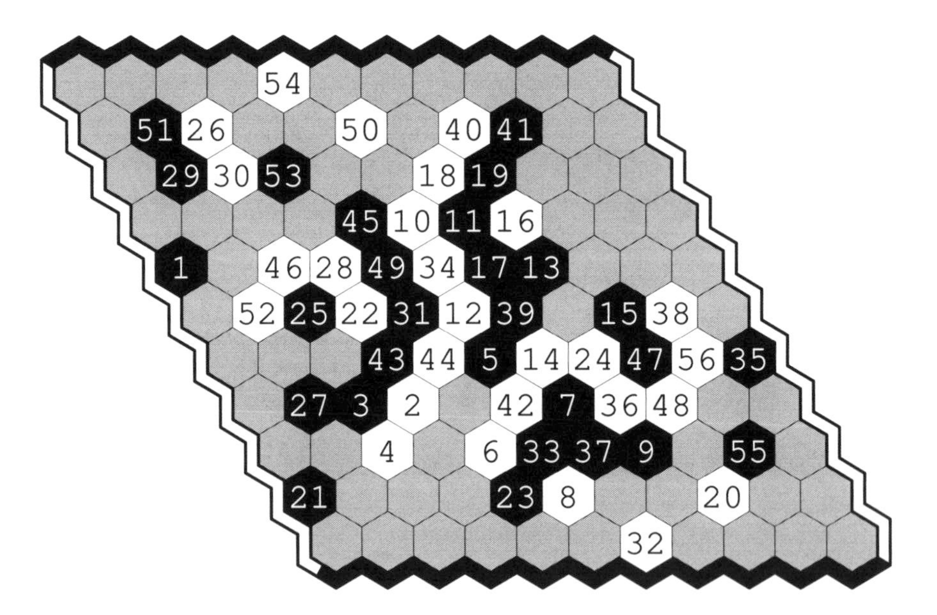

Figure 8.5. MoHex-2.0 (B) vs MoHex-CNN (W).

8.3 simple player

Have you ever written a game-playing computer program? Try it! Here's a fun first task: take as input a Hex position and generate as output a uniformly-randomly chosen empty cell. For a position with 13 empty cells, your program should pick each cell on average 1/13th of the time.

Here's a second task: convert your random-empty-cell-picker into a good-move-picker, like this. Consider a position, say with B to play. Make a random B-move. Did that move win? If not, make a random W-move. Did that move win? If not, continue to alternate random B- and W-moves until you make a move that wins. Record the winner, B or W, and the winning cell. Why the winning cell? Because that cell — unlike all other cells in the random game you just played — is guaranteed to be in a minimal winset, and we know from Chapter 5 that cells in minimal winsets are useful. Repeat this trial some number of times — say 1,000,000 — and then pick the cell that won for B most often as your B-move. Now you have your first computer Hex player!

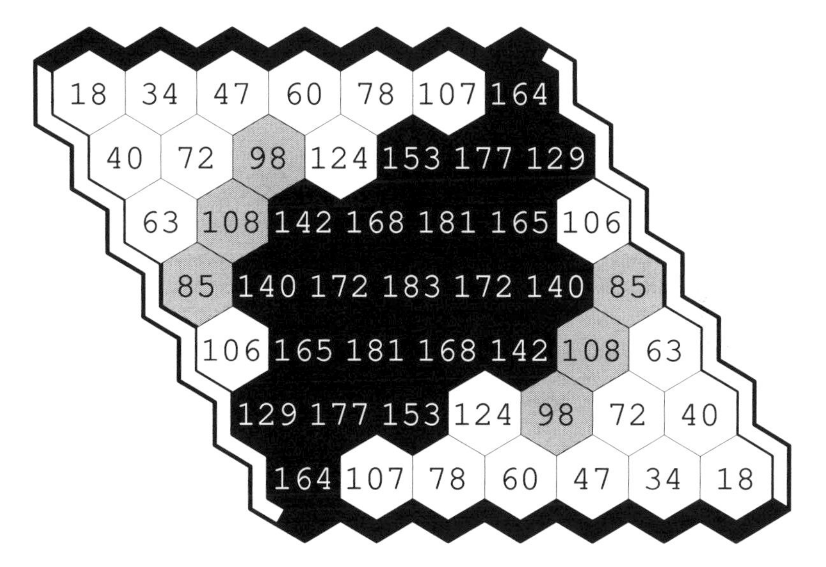

Figure 8.6. Cell-wins-for-B rates ($\times 10^4$) after 5×10^7 uniform-random games. Black cell: rate ≥ 0.0129. Black/gray cell: B-wins opening move.

Figure 8.6 shows how often each cell won for B in 50,000,000 random games on the empty 7×7 board. (In case you are wondering, B won 0.544 of the games.) The two acute corners were the least useful cells, each the winning move in about .0018 of the games (91,543 for the upper left, 91,190 for the lower right). The center was the most useful cell, winning in about

.0183 of the games (915,470). Our computer Hex player would have picked the center cell as the first move in this game — a winning 7×7 opening move! (This might also be the 7×7 opening move that wins quickest.) Our recorded winrates are rotationally symmetric, so these sampled values have perhaps started converging to the true expected values.

Like Shannon's electric resistance circuit, our most-winning-cell player is a good predictor of empty-board opening move strength. Each of the top 21 cells by winrate (0.0129 or more) is a winning first move, and each of the bottom 16 cells (0.078 or less) is a losing first move. Of the remaining 12 cells, the six gray cells in the figure are winning first moves.

8.4 trick player

In addition to his resistance Hex machine — and another resistance machine he built for a game called Bridg-It, also called Birdcage [**19**] — Shannon built a trick Hex machine [**20**] that never lost a game! Its board is shown in Figure 8.7. Can you figure out how it always won? Answer on the next page.

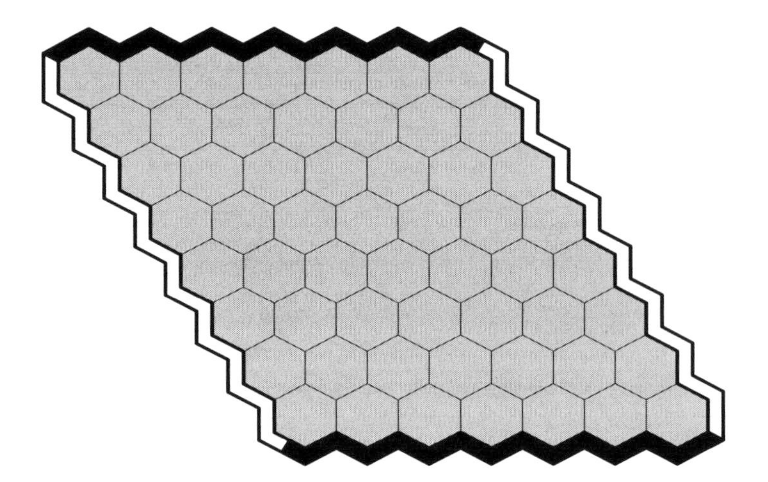

Figure 8.7. The board from Shannon's unbeatable Hex machine. The opponent plays first as B, the machine plays second as W. The machine always wins! Can you see why?

Shannon's trick machine uses a 7×8 board disguised to look regular! After each human move, the machine flashes a light for a few seconds — suggesting that it is thinking — and then lights up the cell for its next move, which it finds instantly with a wiring of the 7×8 pairing strategy we saw in Chapter 2.

Shannon's trick machine raises a disturbing question. For irregular Hex, there is an easy way to win: maybe this also holds for regular boards? We cannot prove that no such easy winning way exists, but there is circumstantial evidence against it.

In 1984 the mathematician Stefan Reisch proved that the problem of solving arbitrary Hex positions belongs to a class of hard problems — called P-space complete — with this property: if we find an efficient (polynomial-time) method to solve it, then we can efficiently solve thousands of other problems [**35**]. The circumstantial evidence that no such method exists is that these other hard problems have collectively been studied by thousands of scientists over several decades and so far no one has found an efficient way to solve any of them.

What does this mean for you? Two things. One, don't be bothered if you find some Hex puzzles are hard to solve, so does everyone else. Two, if you find an efficient way to solve arbitrary Hex puzzles, then you should publish your method, because you will be famous! And you will have money to spend. If a polynomial-time Hex-puzzle-solver exists, then the question "does P equal NP?" has answer "yes". This is a Clay Millenium Prize question, and for answering it the Clay foundation will pay you one million dollars.

9

uniform random Hex

Everything in nature happens in a mathematical way.

René Descartes

Watson: *You may be right.*
Holmes: *The probability lies in that direction.*

Arthur Conan Doyle, in *Hound of the Baskervilles*

You can learn a lot from random processes. The Count of Buffon asked this over 200 years ago: if you drop a needle onto the floor, and the floor is covered with parallel wood strips, each the same width, and the length of the needle equals the width of these strips, what is the probability that the needle crosses the edge of some strip? The answer turns out to be 2 over pi, where pi is of course the ratio of a circle's circumference to its diameter. You can use a random process to estimate a fixed constant, in this case the ratio pi.

What can random processes tell us about Hex? In the previous chapter we saw that randomly sampling Hex moves from minimal winsets gives a good indication of move strength. In this chapter we will explain why the game of uniform random Hex — each player's every move is uniformly random — is surprisingly fair.

9.1 2×2

Let's start small. In a uniform random 2×2 Hex game, what is the probability that the first player wins? Answer on the next page.

In Hex, the game ends as soon as one of the players joins their two edges. In uniform-random Hex, let's continue to play until the board is full: this doesn't change the outcome and it simplifies analysis. In particular, it's not hard to prove that playing uniform-random Hex game is the same as uniform-randomly picking a permutation of the board cells and playing the game in the usual Black-White-Black-White-Black-White ... order.

Figure 9.1 shows the 24 permutations of the four cells of the 2×2 board and the winner of each corresponding game. Black wins 12 times, White wins 12 times. In 2×2 uniform-random Hex, each player wins with probability 1/2.

(1,2,3,4) B	(2,1,3,4) B	(3,1,2,4) B	(4,1,2,3) B
(1,2,4,3) W	(2,1,4,3) B	(3,1,4,2) W	(4,1,3,2) W
(1,3,2,4) W	(2,3,1,4) W	(3,2,1,4) B	(4,2,1,3) W
(1,3,4,2) W	(2,3,4,1) B	(3,2,4,1) W	(4,2,3,1) W
(1,4,2,3) W	(2,4,1,3) W	(3,4,1,2) B	(4,3,1,2) W
(1,4,3,2) B	(2,4,3,1) B	(3,4,2,1) B	(4,3,2,1) B

Figure 9.1. For each Black-White-Black-White move sequence, winner of that 2×2 game.

In uniform-random Hex, the order of moves does not matter: what matters is only which cells are assigned to which player. For example, in Figure 9.1 move sequences (1,2,3,4), (1,4,3,2), (3,2,1,4), (3,4,1,2) all have the same outcome — B (Black) wins — because in each case B gets cells {1,3} and W gets cells {2,4}. Here is a way to think of 2×2 uniform-random Hex: the first player gets a uniform-random subset of two of the four cells of the board, the other player gets the other cells. Figure 9.2 shows all possible 2×2 games viewed in this way. There are six two-element subsets of a four element set. Three of those subsets are B-winsets, so B wins with probability 3/6, or 1/2.

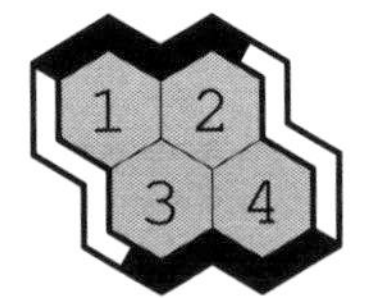

{1,2} W	{1,3} B	{1,4} W
{2,3} B	{2,4} B	{3,4} W

Figure 9.2. For each 2-element set of black-colored cells, winner of that 2×2 game.

9.2 3×3

Let's try a larger board. Using what we have seen, can you find the first-player win probability for 3×3 uniform-random Hex? Answer on the next page.

Again, we can assume that play continues until the board is full. Thus for the first player, playing a uniform-random one-move-at-a-time 3×3 Hex is equivalent to playing uniform-random pick-all-moves-at-once. There are 9 choose 5 (equals 126) 5-element subsets of a 9-set: 84 of these subsets join the top of the board to the bottom, so the first player wins 84/126 (equals 2/3) of the time. Hex has no draws, so the second player wins 1/3 of the time.

Another way to think of this problem is to consider all possible move sequences of a game. Since each player moves uniform-randomly, each possible game sequence is equally likely to occur. There are 9 factorial (equals 362,880) permutations of a 9-set. Using a computer, you can check that exactly 2/3 of these sets win for the first player.

We can use move sequences to answer another question: for each possible move number 1 to 9, what is the probability that a uniform-random 3×3 game ends on that move?

For moves 1 through 4, the answer is 0: each player needs at least three stones to win, and after move 4 each player has only two stones on the board. What about move 5? On that move the first player, say B, has 3 stones and the second player has 2. With move 5, the first player's 3-stone subset is equally likely to be any of the 9 choose 3 (equals 84) 3-cell subsets of the 9 cells. Figure 9.3 shows the 8 of these subsets that win for B. Thus the probability that the game ends on move 5 is 8/84, or 2/21.

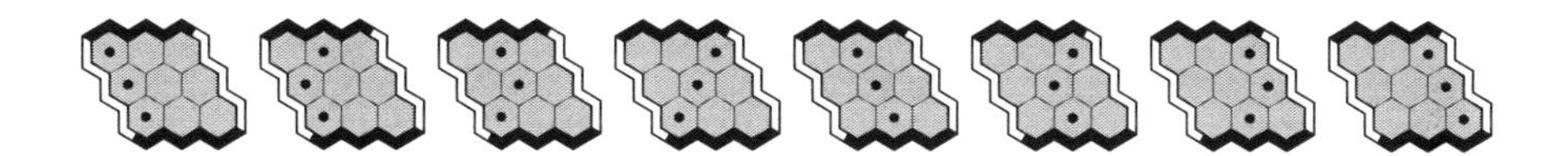

Figure 9.3. All B-winning 3-cell subsets.

We leave it to you to prove this: on move 6, W's 3-stone subset is equally likely to be any of the 84 3-cell subsets of the 9 cells. Again, 8 of these subsets are W-winsets, so the probability that the game ends on move 6 is the same that it ends on move 5, namely 2/21.

What about move 7? We won't show them to you, but 42 of the 126 4-cell subsets of the 9 cells are B-winsets, so by move 7 (on move 5 or on move 7) B wins with probability 42/126 (equals 1/3). We have seen that B wins on move 5 with probability 2/21, thus B wins on move 7 with probability $1/3 - 2/21 = 5/21$.

W wins on move 8 with the same probability that B wins on move 7, so 5/21. That leaves the remainder of probability for the last move: B wins on move 9 with probability $1 - (2+2+5+5)/21 = 7/21 = 1/3$. See Figure 9.4.

move number	5	6	7	8	9
win prob. on that move	2/21	2/21	5/21	5/21	7/21

Figure 9.4. 3×3 win probability, by move.

9.3 n even

Uniform-random Hex on any $n \times n$ board with n even is a fair game: each player's win probability is exactly 1/2. Can you see why?

We'll give the argument for the 2×2 board, but it holds for any $n \times n$ board with n an even number. Consider the subset point of view: one player, say B, wins if and only if the random subset of cells assigned to B — here 2 cells, in general $n \times n/2$ cells — is a B-winset. How can we prove that exactly half of these subsets are B-winsets? By pairing off all subsets so that exactly one subset is B-winning.

Here's how to pair these subsets. Take any B-winset, say S. The set of cells not in S, say T, is the same size as S, and is losing set for W (because one and only one player wins any filled-board position). To find the equivalent losing set U for B, take the mirror reflection through the short diagonal (obtuse corner to obtuse corner). In this way, each B-winset has a mate, and every mate is B-losing, so this partitions all of these subsets. Figure 9.5 shows this pairing for the 2×2 board. Thus, for any even n, exactly half of all the $(n \times n)/2$-subsets are B-winning.

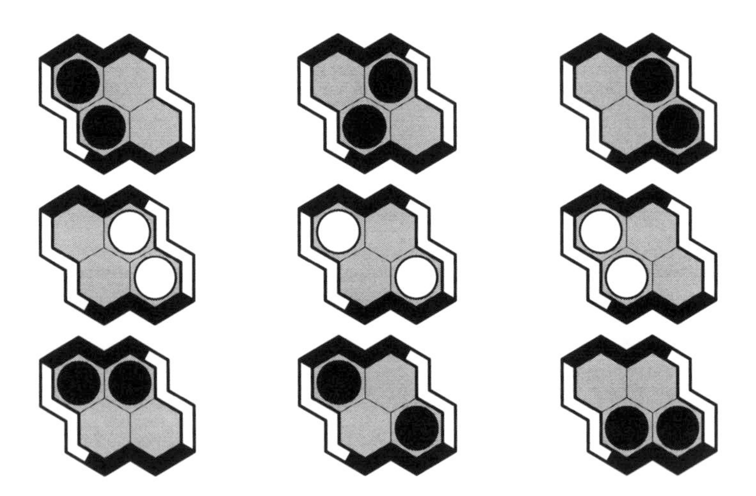

Figure 9.5. Pair each B-winning subset (top row), through its W-losing set-complement (middle row), with the complement's B-losing short-diagonal reflection (bottom row).

9.4 n odd

What about odd n? Here's what we know.

If on some move the first player wins with probability p, and if the board is not full, then on the next move the second player also wins with probability p. For $n \times n$ boards with n odd, the win-on-move-k probabilities form a sequence $(p, p, q, q, \ldots, y, y, z)$ and the first-player's win probability will be z more than the second-player's. We saw earlier that on the 3×3 board the first player wins on the last move with probability 1/3. Thus over all previous moves, each player wins with probability $(1-1/3)/2 = 1/3$, so the first- and second-players winrates (winning probabilities) are $1/3$ and $1/3 + 1/3 = 2/3$ respectively.

n	3	5	7	9	11	13	15	17	19	21
winrate	.667	.573	.544	.531	.523	.518	.515	.513	.511	.510

Figure 9.6. $n \times n$ rand.-Hex 1st-player winrates.

Figure 9.6 shows estimated first-player uniform-random-Hex winrates on odd boards up to 21×21, based on 1,000,000 games per board. You can compute these values exactly for the 3×3 and 5×5 boards, 1/3 and 2981241/5200300 = 0.573... respectively. Just for fun, we estimated the winrate-by-move for uniform-random Hex on the 21×21 board. See Figure 9.7.

In math there are often more questions than answers. Here are a few open uniform-random Hex questions to play around with.

- For $n \times n$ boards with n odd, the probability that the game does not end until the board is filled is positive (can you see why?), so the first-player-wins probability is greater than 1/2. Does the limit of this probability as n grows exist? If yes, is it 1/2?

- In Figure 9.7, it looks like the probability that the game ends on move 441 is less than the probability that it ends on move 439? Is this correct, or just an anomaly because our sampled data has not yet started converging to the final correct values? For all n, is the probability that the game ends on move k monotonically increasing? If no, what is the smallest board size, and smallest move number, where this does not hold?

9.5 deterministic versus random

A *deterministic* player — possibly a human, possibly a computer program — is the opposite of a random player: it ranks moves based on some kind of evaluation system, and always makes what it judges to be a best move. Bruce Reed, a graph theorist at McGill University and the French National Center for Scientific Research, asked this: what happens when a deterministic player

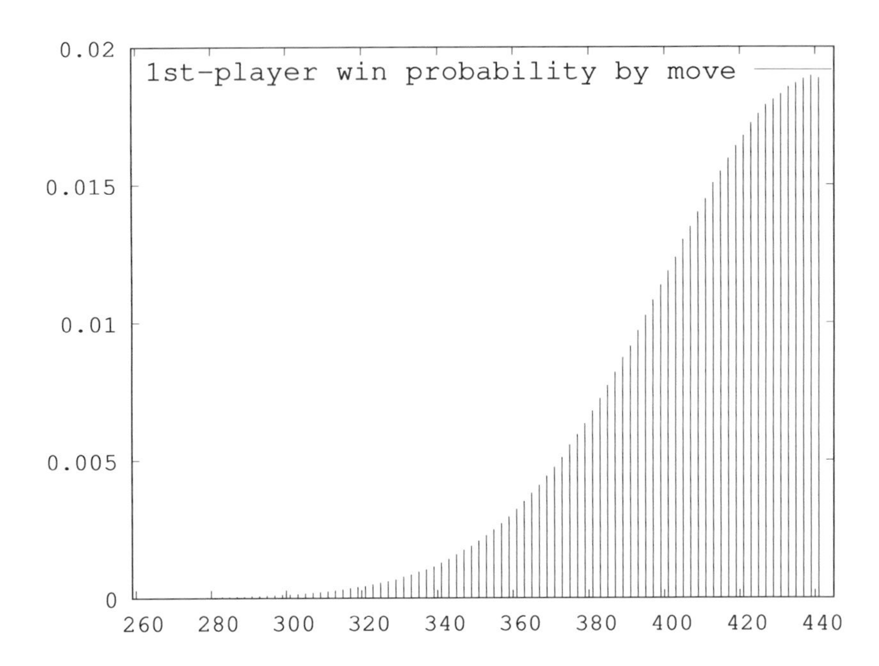

Figure 9.7. 21×21 win probability by move.

D plays a uniform-random player R? On a regular board D will likely win, but what happens on an irregular board whose shape favors R?

As a warm-up, consider the regular 2×2 board in Figure 9.8. Assume that R plays first with black stones and edges and that D plays second with white stones and edges. So we will call the players by their full names, RB and DW. To see how big the gap in playing strength between RB and DW can be, let's further assume that DW plays perfectly, always picking a move that maximizes its expected winrate.

If RB opens at an acute corner, say a1, then DW blocks with a2, so DW has a winning virtual connection and RW wins with probability 0. If RB opens at an obtuse corner, say a2, then DW takes a1 or b1: in each case, RB wins with probability 1/2. Each RB-opening move is equally likely, so RB's expected 2×2 winrate is 1/4. Can you work out these probabilities for the 2×3 and 2×4 boards? Answer on the next page.

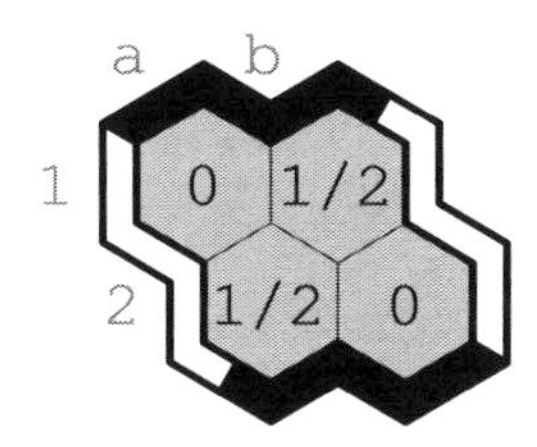

Figure 9.8. After each first move by random player RB, expected winrate for RB.

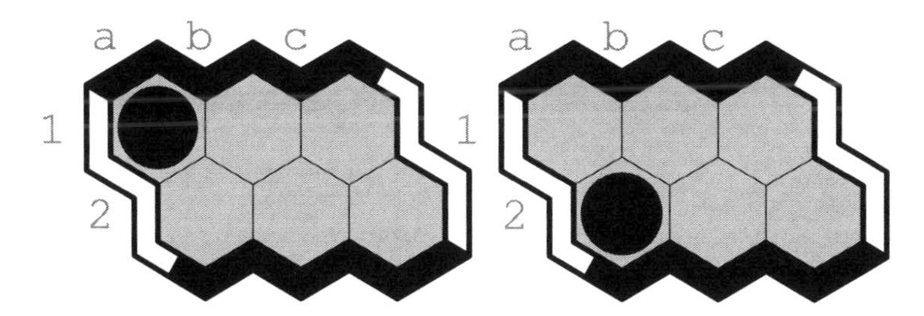

Figure 9.9. In each case, find a best reply for the deterministic player DW.

Let's consider the 2×3 board. After RB plays 1.B[a1] as shown in Figure 9.9, a best reply for DW is 2.W[a2]. Why?

After 1.B[a1], RB has the 1-move winset {a2}. Whenever RB has a 1-move winset, a best reply for DW is to play at that cell. This takes a bit of care to prove. Assume that the winset is $\{ \alpha \}$ and consider any deterministic strategy X that starts by playing at some location β instead of α. Transform X to X' by switching α and β. In some continuation of the game under S, if the random player wins with a final set of cells S, then they also win with the set S' obtained from S by interchanging α and β — can you see why? RB's expected winrate against X' is no better than against X.

After 1.B[a1] 2.W[a2], DW wins only by joining b1 or b2 to the right edge, so a best W-strategy now is the same as on the 2×2 board. Thus 1.B[a1] wins with probability 1/4.

Similarly, after 1.B[a2], a best W-reply is 2.W[a1]. Now 3.W[b1] wins instantly, 3.W[c1] will win, and 3.W[b2] and 3.W[c3] will each win with probability 1/2, so 1.B[a2] wins with probability 3/4.

Can you work the winning probability for each of the other four first moves for RB? Answer on the next page.

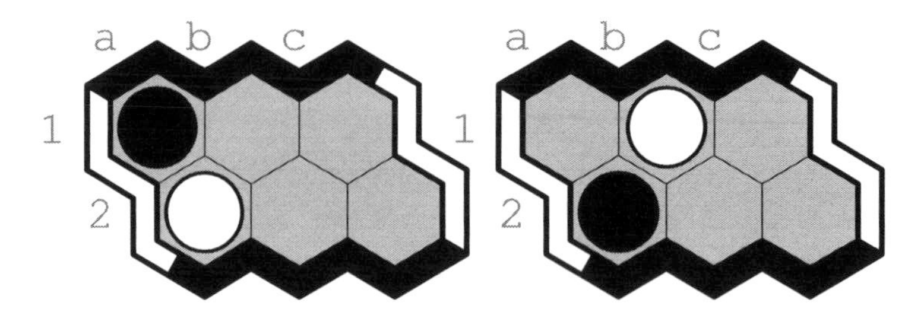

Figure 9.10. Best DW-replies. 1.B[a1] and 1.B[a2] win with probability 1/4 and 3/4 respectively.

Figure 9.11. After each first move by random player RB, expected winrate for RB.

As you can see in Figure 9.11, the opening-move winrates form a simple sequence: along each row of the $2{\times}n$ board, cell k (counting the obtuse corner) wins with probability $1 - k/2^{n-1}$. Why?

Consider an RB-move in the $2{\times}n$ game, say to row x — 1 or 2 — and column y. If the move does not win, then the other cell in that column is empty, and also a B-winset with size 1. A best strategy for DW is to always reply in the same column where RB just played. In this game, RB is randomly picking which row each stone will be in. To see what happens, we only need to know which stone in each column is the B-stone. For example, on the $2{\times}n$ board, after RB opens at a2, DW replies at b1, and DW wins only if each remaining RB-move is in the bottom column. This happens with probability 1/2 to the power $n-1$. We leave it to you to get from here to the final formula of $1 - k/2^{n-1}$.

Summing RB's win-probability over each possible opening move, B's expected winrate on the $2{\times}n$ board is $1 - (n+1)/2^n$. As n gets large, RB's expected winrate gets arbitrarily close to 1.

Recently Reed together with Jordan Barrett, Noah Brustle, Sarah Clusiau, Vishnu Narayan and Ndiame Ndiaye showed that on the $5{\times}n$ board the deterministic player can play so that the random player's winrate goes to 0. It's not yet known what happens on the $3{\times}n$ or $4{\times}n$ boards.

10

dark Hex

Everyone is a moon, and has a dark edge that they never show to anybody.
Mark Twain

If you like battleships or poker you might enjoy Dark Hex, also called Kriegspiel Hex or Phantom Hex. The game has two players and a referee. Each player sees their own moves: the referee sees all moves. On a turn, a player privately asks the referee whether a particular cell is empty. If yes, the player moves there. If no, the player — who now knows that the opponent has a stone there — tries again, and keeps trying until successfully making a move.

10.1 sample game and tip

Figure 10.1 shows the first two moves of a 3×3 game. Black opens 1.B[b2].

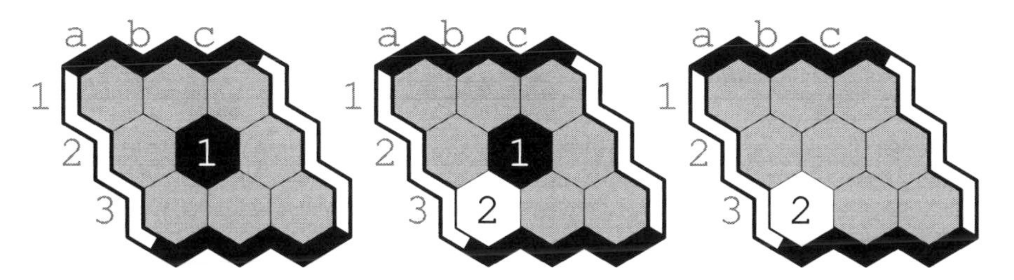

Figure 10.1. Black sees the left board, the referee sees the middle board, White sees the right board.

White then asks the referee about a3 — it is empty — and plays 2.W[a3]. The game continues 3.B[c1] 4.W[b3]. On move 5, Black tries a3 (occupied), b3 (occupied), and c3: we write this as 5.B[a3,b3,c3]. The game is now as in Figure 10.2. Who will win?

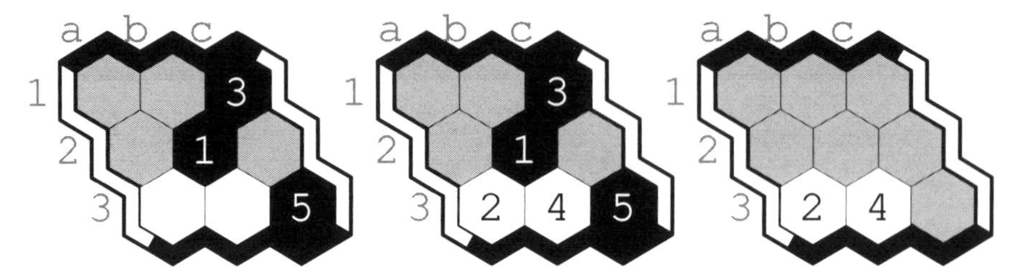

Figure 10.2. Game in progress: Black sees the left board, White sees the right board.

White wins! Do you see why? Here is a Dark Hex tip: if some cell with unknown status (empty or with an as-yet-unseen opponent stone) joins your edges, try it! If the cell is empty, you win; if the cell is occupied, you can try again. In Figure 10.2 it's White's turn, both c2 and c3 will win for White, so White tries these two cells first: c2 is empty, so White wins.

10.2 2×2 and mixed strategies

Let's analyze 2×2 Dark Hex. Can you find a best strategy for each player? Assume Black plays first.

Opening at an obtuse corner wins. For example, if Black opens 1.B[a2] as in Figure 10.3, then after White's move at least one of {a1,b1} is empty, so 3.B[a1,b1] wins by the Dark Hex tip.

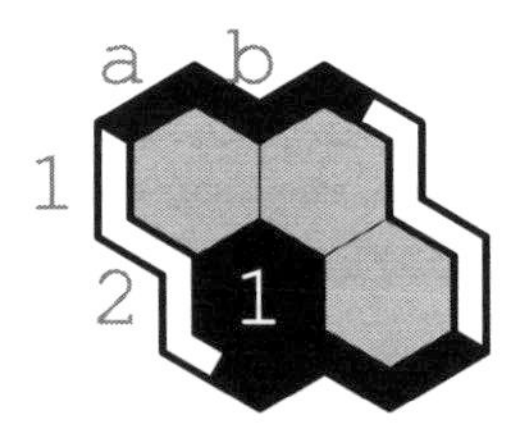

Figure 10.3. This Black opening wins.

How should White play in case Black's opens at one of the acute corners, as indicated in Figure 10.4? White's two possible strategies are 2.W[a2] 4.W[b1,b2] or 2.W[b1] 4.W[a1,a2]. The former wins against 1.B[a1] 3.B[a2], the latter against 1.B[b2] 3.B[b1]. Which strategy should White pick?

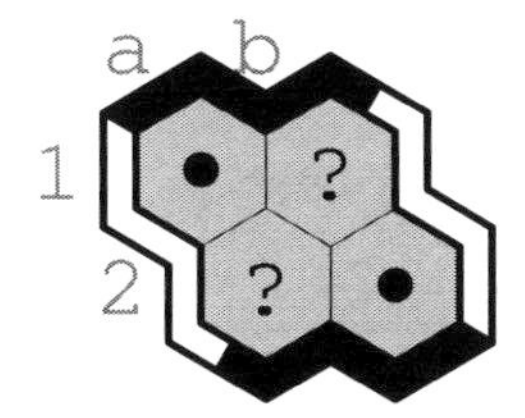

Figure 10.4. How should White reply in case Black opens at an acute corner?

So far, each strategy in this book has been *fixed*, or *deterministic*: for each position, the required move is always the same. (A strategy is a function that maps reachable positions to moves: it always maps a particular input to the same output.) In Dark Hex, unless you have a sure win, don't follow a fixed strategy: the opponent will learn to defeat it. Instead, follow a *mixed strategy* that randomly combines fixed strategies.

For the position in Figure 10.4, White should flip a coin! If the coin comes up heads, play 2.W[a2] as in Figure 10.5. If the coin comes up tails, play 2.W[b1]. If each flip outcome is equally likely, White's mixed strategy — composed of two fixed strategies each played with probability .5 — wins with probability .5 against each of Black's acute-corner opening moves.

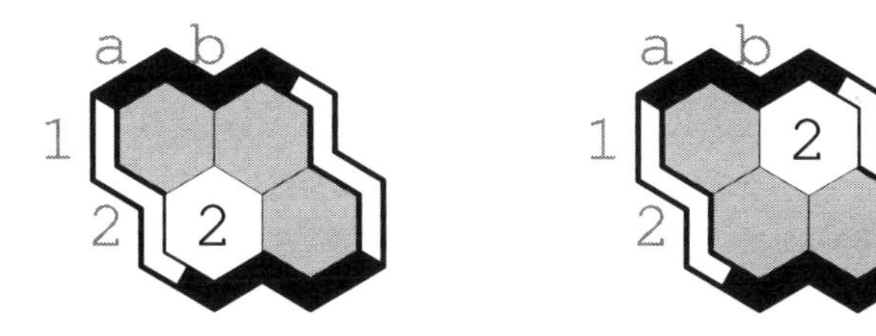

Figure 10.5. Play each strategy half the time.

If you have not seen mixed strategies before, take a look at *Game Theory, A Playful Introduction* by Matt DeVos and Deborah A. Kent [**12**]. It explains mixed strategies and other cool stuff on game theory, including two chapters on Hex with a Hex-has-no-draws proof using Sperner's lemma.

10.3 3×3 and minimax

Now that we know about mixed strategies, let's look at 3×3 positions. In 1979 William McWorter Jr. posed two Dark Hex problems in *Mathematics Magazine*: prove that the first player (1) can always win on the 3×3 board but (2) cannot always win on any larger $n \times n$ board.

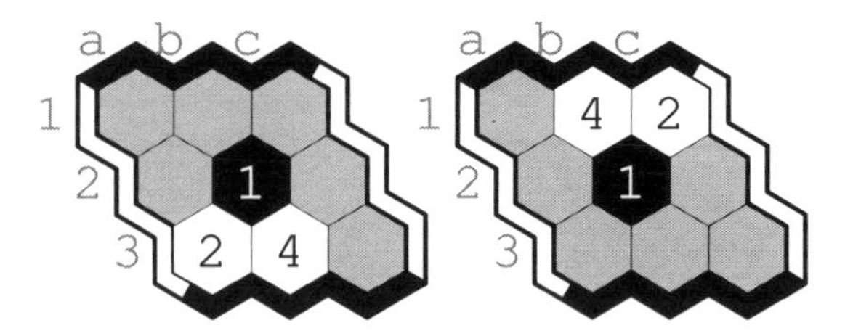

Figure 10.6. Play each strategy half the time.

We will address these problems in this chapter. For now, what is your guess for the first move in an always-winning 3×3 Dark Hex strategy? It's not the center! The white mixed strategy in Figure 10.6 wins half the time against the center opening. If Black's move 3 is to any of {a1, a2, b1, c1} then the left white strategy wins: 2.W[a3] succeeds, 4.W[b3] succeeds, and one of 6.W[c2], 6.W[c3] succeeds. By rotational symmetry, if Black's move 3 is to any of {a3, b3, c2, c3} then the right white strategy wins.

We'll return to the search for an always-winning Black opening move shortly. For now, let's continue our discussion about the 3×3 Dark Hex center opening: if Black's first move is there, how should Black continue?

After opening 1.B[b2], assume that Black becomes risk averse and wants to minimize how well White can do. For every fixed black strategy there is a white counter-strategy that wins all the time, so Black must pick a mixed strategy. Over all possible mixed strategies, Black wants a mixed strategy that minimizes — over all possible White counter-strategies — White's expected winrate. We call such a strategy a *minimax* strategy: it minimizes the maximum score that the opponent can achieve. After opening in the center, what is a black minimax strategy?

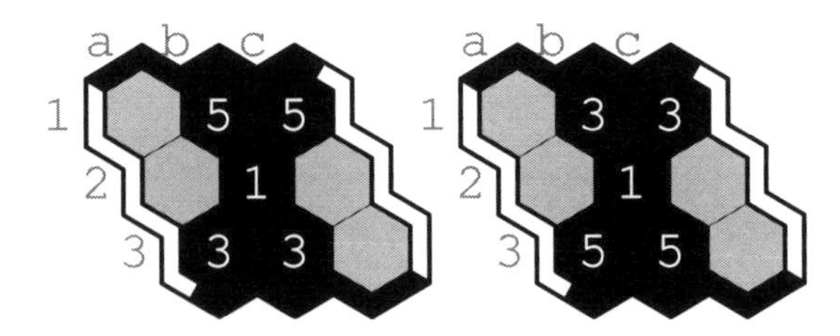

Figure 10.7. Play each strategy half the time.

Consider this black strategy S: *equi-mix* (play each strategy the same fraction of the time) the two fixed strategies 1.B[b2] 3.B[a3,b3] 5.B[b1,c1] and 1.B[b2] 3.B[b1,c1] 5.B[a3,b3] shown in Figure 10.7. White blocks the former strategy only with the left strategy in Figure 10.6, and blocks the latter strategy only with the right strategy. No matter how White plays, White's expected winrate is at most .5.

We saw earlier that after Black opens in the center, Black wins at most half the time when White equi-mixes the strategies in Figure 10.6. Now we see that Black wins at least half the time with S. Thus S is a Black minimax strategy, and Black's minimax expected winrate is exactly .5

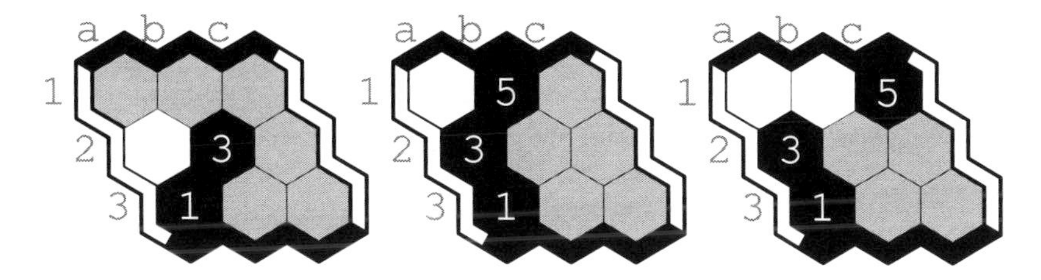

Figure 10.8. 1st-player-wins strategy.

Now let's return to McWorter's first problem: for 3×3 Dark Hex, how can the first player always win? As in Figure 10.8, open in an obtuse corner! Black starts 1.B[a3] 3.B[a2,b2]. After 2.W[a2], 3.B[b2] succeeds and 5.B[b1,c1] wins (left diagram). After 3.B[a2] Black continues 5.B[a1,b1,c1], winning if a1 or b1 (middle diagram) succeed. If both fail then there are white stones at {a1, b1}, 5.B[c1] succeeds (right diagram), and 7.B[b2,c2] or — if 7.B[b2] fails — 9.B[b3,c3] wins.

The diagram in Figure 10.9 also shows this strategy: each node represents a game position, and each node's children — from left to right — show Black's sequence of move requests. The top node is the starting position: from there, Black plays 1.B[a3]. Next Black tries a2 and then if necessary b2, and so on.

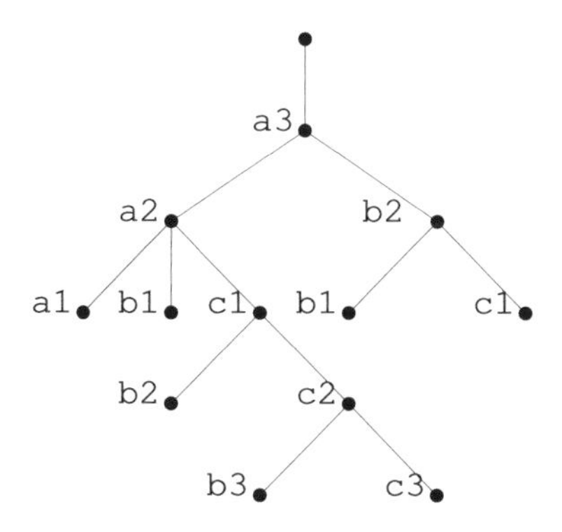

Figure 10.9. 1st-player-wins strategy diagram.

10.4 three easy puzzles

Let's take a break for some puzzles. Each player sees all stones played so far. Can Black always win? Can White? Answers below.

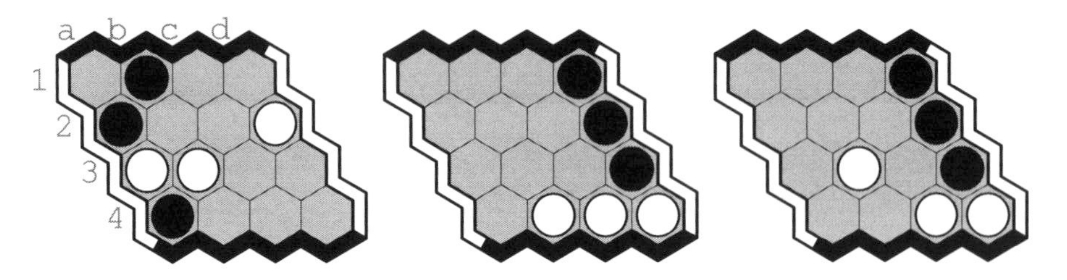

Figure 10.10. Black to play.

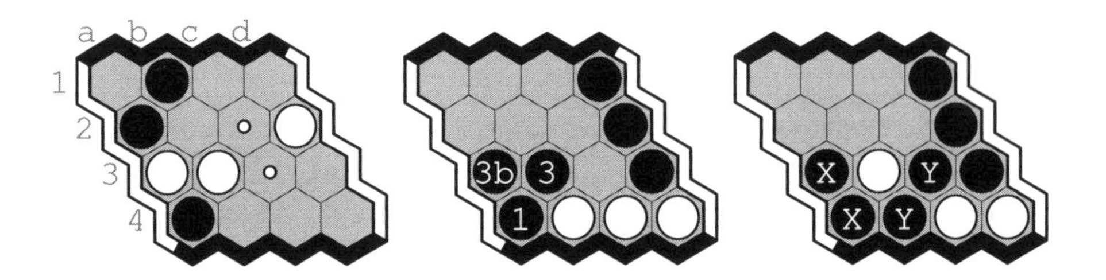

Figure 10.11. From left, Black winrate 0, 1, .5.

In the left puzzle of Figure 10.11, Black's winrate is 0. White wins with the bridge (dots); try one cell; if occupied, try the other cell.

In the middle puzzle, Black wins with probability 1 by playing 1.B[a4] 3.B[b3,a3]. After 3.B[b3] play 5.B[c2,c3,b2] and 7.B[b1,c1] if needed. After 3.B[a3] play 3.B[a3] 5.B[b2,a2]. After 5.B[b2], 7.B[b1,c1,c2] wins. After 5.B[a2], 7.B[a1,b1] wins.

In the right puzzle, White has bridges {a3,a4} (X) and {b4,c3} (Y). B1 is the strategy where Black first takes both X-cells. B2 is the strategy where Black first takes both Y-cells and then continues as in the middle puzzle. White defeats B1 only with strategy W1: take a Y-cell, then an X-cell. Black defeats W1 with strategy B2. White defeats B2 with strategy W2: take a Y-cell, then an X-cell. Black mixes B1 and B2 and wins half the time. White mixes W1 and W2 and wins half the time.

10.5 larger boards

Let's return to McWorter's second problem, solved by Duane Broline at the University of Evansville [**7**]. For 4×4 Dark Hex neither player can always win. Why? Figure 10.10 gives a hint. In the left and right puzzles, Black's first three moves leave room for White to place three stones that join White's edges with at most two bridges. If White needs only one bridge to join, White wins by trying both cells on her next move. If White needs two bridges to join, White wins at least half the time by mixing the order in which she tries to join the bridges.

No matter how Black places her first three stones, White has a three-stone counter-strategy with positive winrate against those three Black stones. By mixing all such counter-strategies, White has positive winrate. A similar argument holds for larger boards. Thus, for $n \times n$ boards with n at least 4, neither player can always win.

What about 3×4 Dark Hex? When the first player's edges are three cells apart, the first player's winrate is 1 (as on the 3×3 board). When these edges are four cells apart, each player has positive winrate. As far as I know, no one has yet found the exact first-player-win probability for this problem, nor for the 4×4 board, nor for any larger board.

10.6 solving harder puzzles

Here's how to solve harder Dark Hex puzzles using game theory and some linear programming! You might find this section a bit advanced compared to the rest of this book: feel free to skip it, or maybe come back to it later.

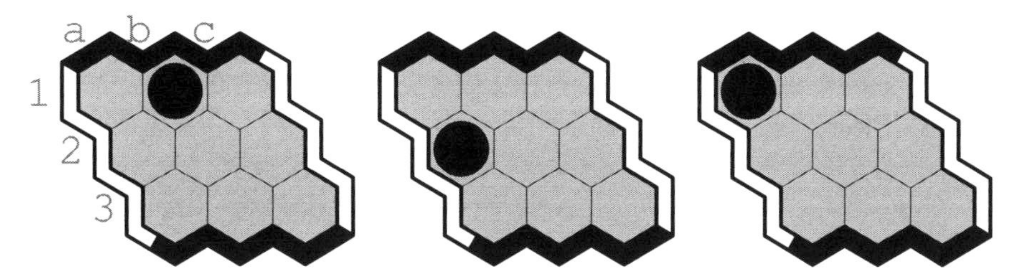

Figure 10.12. White to play.

Figure 10.12 shows three puzzles suggested by François Bonnet — from left, easy, medium, hard: in each puzzle, both players see the initial black stone. For each puzzle, neither player can always win: for each player, can you find a minimax mixed strategy and the associated winrate? We will show you how to solve the medium puzzle, you can try the other puzzles later.

Let's start: assume 1.B[a2] and that White sees this move. It's White's turn: does Black have any threats? If 3.B[a3] succeeds then Black wins with the obtuse-corner-opening strategy. (Here Black plays 1.B[a2] 3.B[a3] instead of 1.B[a3] 3.B[a2], but the rest of the strategy is the same). So White's initial move must be 2.W[a3].

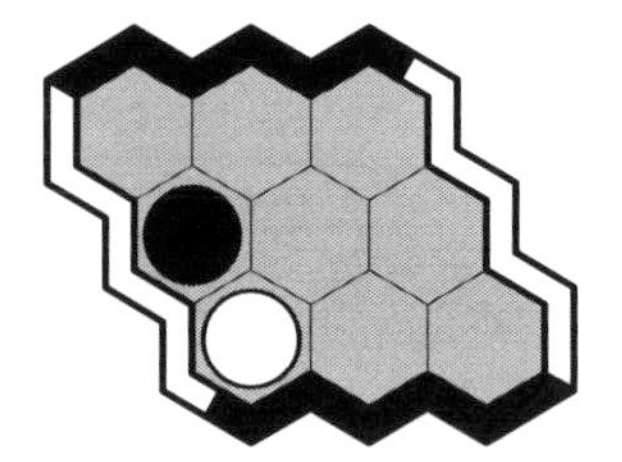

Figure 10.13. Black to play.

Now we have the puzzle in Figure 10.13: Black to play, both players see both stones. Our solving plan has three steps: for each player, (1) find a set of strategies such that every possible opponent strategy loses to at least one strategy in the set; (2) combine some subset of these strategies into a minimax strategy; (3) compute the winrates.

Figure 10.14 shows some promising strategies. In each diagram, the top node represents the starting position in Figure 10.13. Consider the black strategy diagram B_1 (top left). Black starts 3.B[b2] (which succeeds) and 5.B[b3]. If 5.B[b3] fails then White can win so Black makes no further try on move 5. If White does not win by move 6, Black tries 7.B[a1,a2,a3] and wins. Figure 10.15 shows move sequences from these strategies.

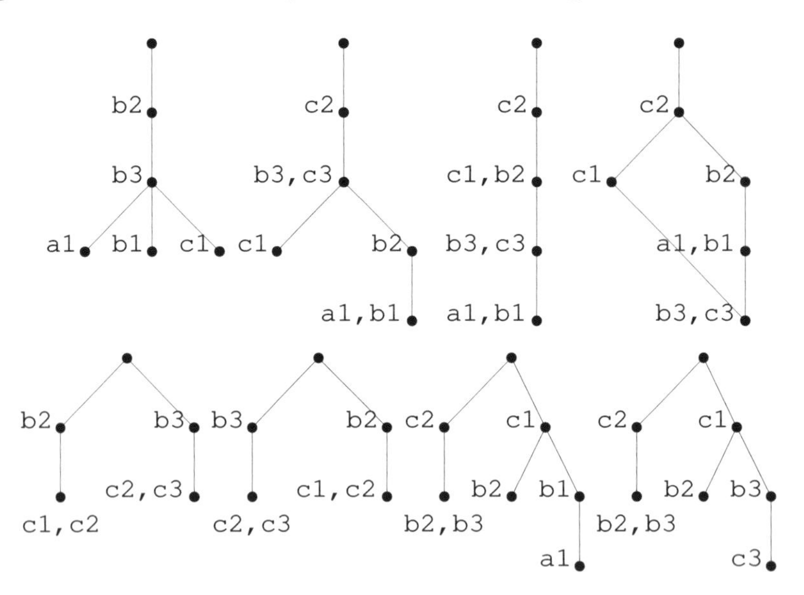

Figure 10.14. Strategy diagrams $B_1, \ldots, B_4$ (top) and $W_1, \ldots, W_4$ (bottom).

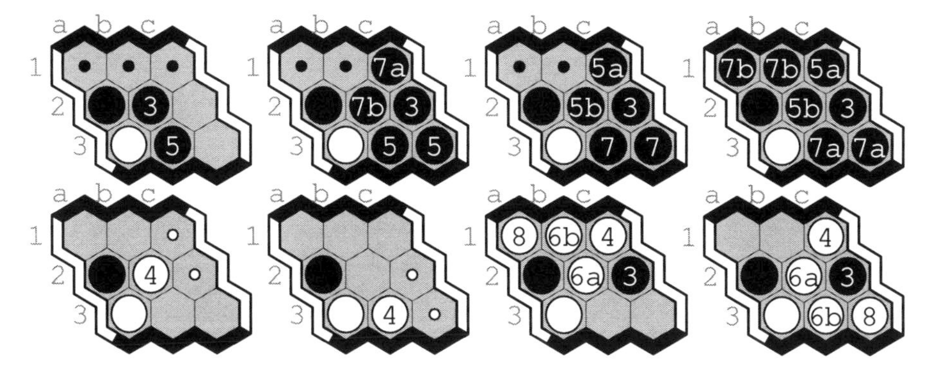

Figure 10.15. Move sequences from $B_1, \ldots, B_4$ (top) and $W_1, \ldots, W_4$ (bottom).

We will not prove it to you — it's a fun logical exercise — but $S_B = \{B_1, \ldots, B_4\}$ and $S_W = \{W_1, \ldots, W_4\}$ satisfy property (1): every legal white strategy is defeated by at least one of $B_1, \ldots, B_4$; every legal black strategy is defeated by at least one of W_1, W_2, W_3. (It turns out that property (1) is all we need to guarantee that the rest of our plan finds us a minimax strategy: we won't prove this either.)

Now we want to use S_B and S_W respectively to find minimax strategies for Black and White. First we need to see how each strategy in S_B performs against each strategy in S_W. We record this information in the *payoff matrix* in Table 10.1.

Table 10.1. Payoff matrix: Black win probability.

	W_1	W_2	W_3	W_4
B_1	0	0	1	1
B_2	0	1	0	0
B_3	1	0	0	1
B_4	1	0	1	0

Next we want to find the weights for the various strategies that will give us our minimax mixed strategies. Here's where we use some game theory. It turns out that when Black plays her minimax strategy, White has an optimal counter-strategy that is fixed! We seek the probabilities with which Black plays $B_1, \ldots, B_4$ — let's call these fractions $b_1, \ldots, b_4$ respectively. These are probabilities, so each is non-negative and their sum is 1.

From the W_1 column of the payoff matrix, we see that Black's expected winrate against W_1 is $r_1 = 0 \times b_1 + 0 \times b_2 + 1 \times b_3 + 1 \times b_4 = b_3 + b_4$. Similarly, using the other columns we find the other expected winrates r_2, r_3, r_4: $r_2 = b_2$,

$r_3 = b_1 + b_4$, $r_4 = b_1 + b_3$. After Black picks her probabilities, White picks the column with smallest Black winrate r_j. So Black chooses $b_1, \ldots, b_4$ to maximize the minimum value in $\{r_1, \ldots, r_4\}$. In other words, Black seeks the largest fraction z so that $z \leq r_1, z \leq r_2, z \leq r_3, z \leq r_4$.

We now have the complete system of equations and inequalities that Black uses to pick $b_1, \ldots, b_4$:

$$\begin{aligned} \max z \quad & \text{so that} \\ z &\leq b_3 + b_4 \\ z &\leq b_2 \\ z &\leq b_1 + b_4 \\ z &\leq b_1 + b_3 \\ 1 &= b_1 + b_2 + b_3 + b_4 \\ b_j &\geq 0 \end{aligned}$$

The variables here are all fractions (rational numbers), so this system is a *linear program* (LP): each constraint is a linear combination of the variables $z, b_1, \ldots, b_4$. Linear programs are easily solved with a fast algorithm called the simplex method: you can find free LP solvers online, for example in the math software system *SageMath* [**11**]. SageMath solves our LP almost instantly: $z = .4, (b_1, \ldots, b_4) = (.2, .4, .2, .2)$.

We leave it to you to formulate an LP to find a white minimax solution: don't forget to switch the 0's and 1's when you construct White's payoff matrix. The solution is $z = .6, (w_1, \ldots, w_4) = (.2, .4, .2, .2)$.

So we have solved the middle puzzle in Figure 10.12. White's minimax solution is to play 2.W[a3] and then mix strategies $W_1, \ldots, W_4$ with probabilites 1/5, 2/5, 1/5, 1/5. By following this strategy, White's expected winrate is always at least 3/5, no matter how Black plays.

Black's minimax solution is to try 3.B[a3] (if this succeeds Black wins by following the usual obtuse corner winning strategy) and if it fails to then mix strategies $B_1, \ldots, B_4$ with probabilities 1/5, 2/5, 1/5, 1/5. By following this strategy, Blacks's expected winrate is always at least 2/5, no matter how White plays.

Now you can try the other two puzzles in Figure 10.12. Partial answers are on the next page.

Figure 10.16 shows the first move probabilities of optimal mixed strategies for the puzzles from Figure 10.12. For the easy puzzle (left), Black can equi-mix 3.B[a3] and 3.B[c2], while White can play 2.W[b2] and then equi-mix 4.W[a2,a3] and 4.W[c1,c2]. In each case, each player wins at least half the time against opponent strategy.

For the hard puzzle (right), Black can mix three strategies — S_1 starts at c1, S_2 starts at b2, S_3 starts at a3 — with respective probabilities 2/5, 1/5, 2/5. Similarly, White can mix two strategies — T_1 starts at a2, T_2 starts at a3 — with probabilities 2/7, 5/7. Black's mixed strategy wins at least 2/7 of the time against any White strategy. White's mixed strategy wins at least 5/7 of the time against any Black strategy.

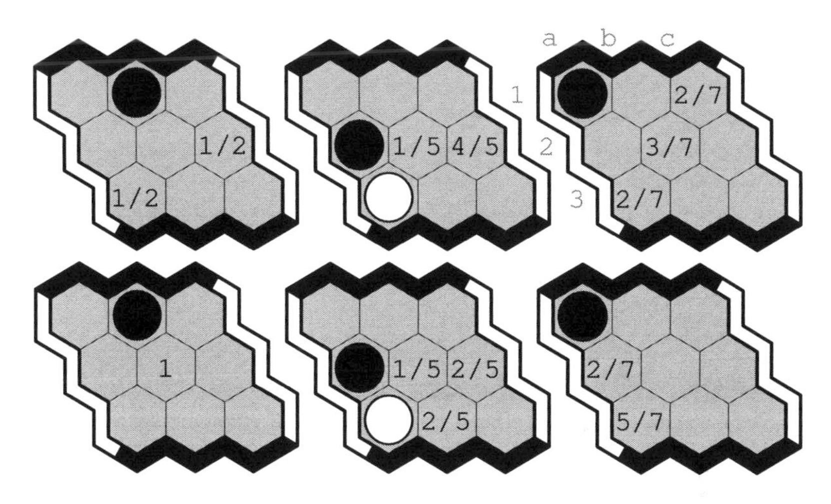

Figure 10.16. First move of optimal strategies (top black, bottom white).

From these puzzles, we now know Black's minimax winrate for the 3×3 board in the special case that White see's Black's first move: see Figure 10.17.

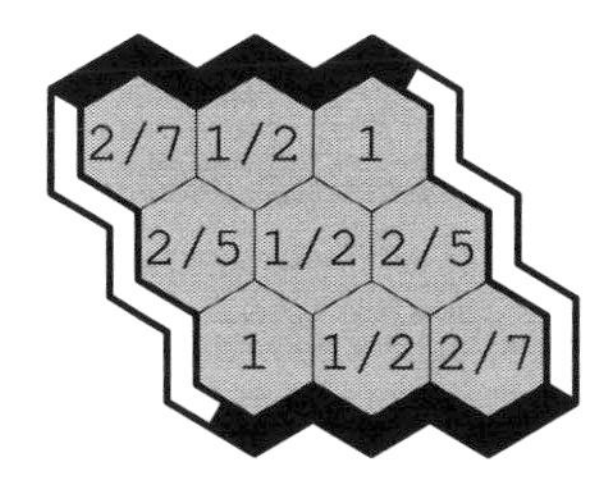

Figure 10.17. Black winrates for each 3×3 B-opening move when W sees that move.

11

larger boards

Understanding the things at our door is the best preparation for understanding the things that lie beyond.

Hypatia

To infinity, and beyond.

Buzz Lightyear

In Figure 11.1, do any of these opening moves win? For each move, what is your best guess, and why?

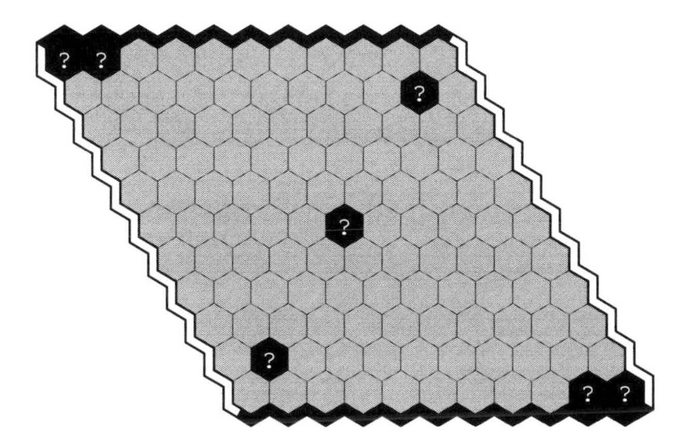

Figure 11.1. Do any of these first moves win?

11.1 evidence

For Hex on the 11×11 (or any larger regular) board, so far no one knows of any particular first-player winning strategy or winning opening move.

Based on circumstantial evidence — the play of Hex experts, resistance network evaluations, cell winrates from uniform-random games — we suspect that the short-diagonal opening moves in Figure 11.1 are winning.

Figure 11.2 shows — for each cell after 50,000,000 uniform-random games — the number of times that cell was a winning B-move divided by the number of games. We guess that any cell whose winrate is at least that of any cell on the short diagonal — colored black in the figure — is a winning first move and that the three short-diagonal cells in Figure 11.1 are the easiest of all cells to prove winning.

We cannot prove any of this.

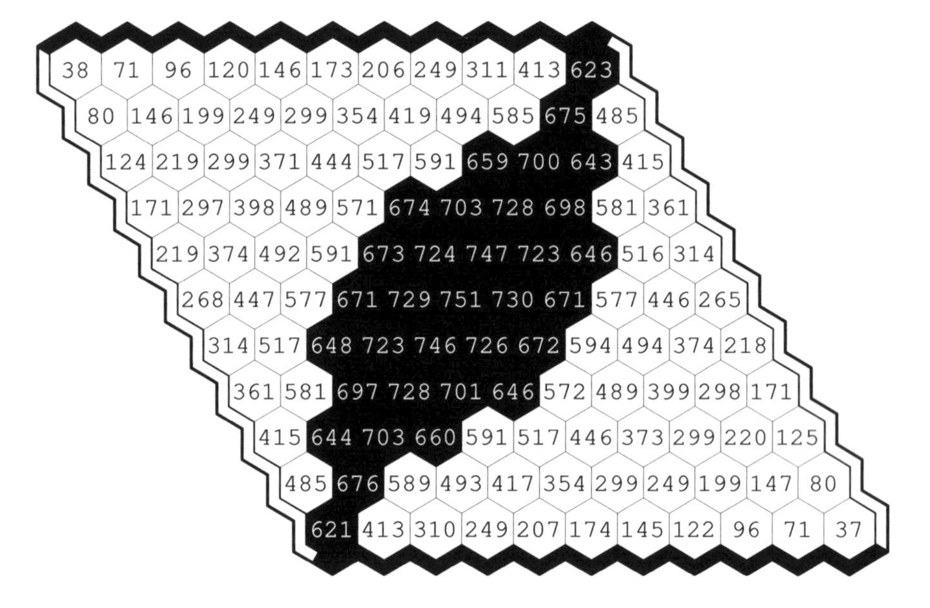

Figure 11.2. Cell-wins-for-B rates (×1000).

However ... we *can* prove that the four opening moves with lowest winrates in Figure 11.2 — shown also in Figure 11.1 — are losing. We explain these proofs now.

11.2 acute corner loses

For Hex on any $n \times n$ board with n at least 2, opening in the acute corner loses. The proof — rewritten in our terminology, using dead and captured sets as defined in Chapter 5 — is by Anatóle Beck, for many years a mathematics professor at the University of Wisconsin. Figure 11.3 hints at the problem with this opening: the opponent can essentially erase it. Beck's proof uses this observation in a clever way.

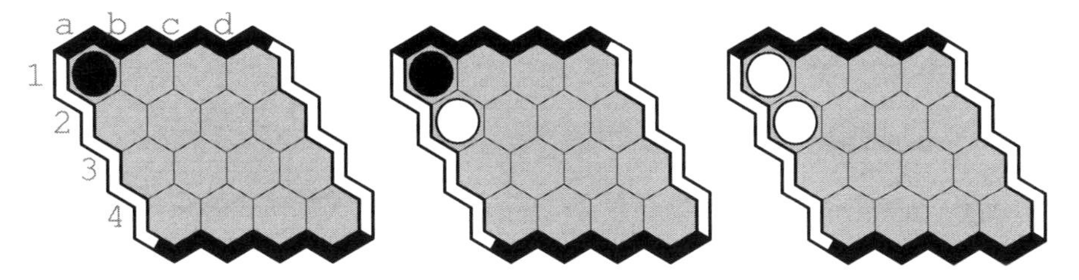

Figure 11.3. Opening, reply, equivalent position.
W's reply effectively erases B's opening move.

Argue by contradiction. Assume that B has a winning strategy S that starts 1.B[a1] as in Figure 11.3. Assume that W replies 2.W[a2]. This erases a1 so, as in the right diagram, W can act as though this dead B-stone is a W-stone.

In the language of Chapter 5, 1.B[a1] is vulnerable to 2.W[a2]. Moving to a vulnerable cell is equivalent to skipping your move, so if 1.B[a1] wins then so does *any* other first move! But to show that 1.B[a1] *loses*, we need something extra: strategy stealing.

W can take B's 1st-player-win strategy S and — after switching its colors and edges — use it herself. The W-stone at a2 — which in the unswitched strategy would be a B-stone at b1 — is extra and so will not wreck this strategy. After 2.W[a2], W has a winning strategy, a contradiction, since now both players can win.

Thus our assumption that S exists is false. After 1.B[a1], B cannot win. Hex has no draws so, after 1.B[a1], B loses. This ends the proof: opening in an acute corner loses.

11.3 acute corner neighbor loses

For any $n \times n$ board with n at least 3, each B-edge-neighbor of an acute corner is a losing B-opening move. Can you guess how this proof goes? Hint: use captured cells as in Figure 11.4.

This proof — again rewritten in our terminology — is by Beck and Charles Holland, for many years a mathematics professor at Bowling Green State University. The proof is similar to the previous proof.

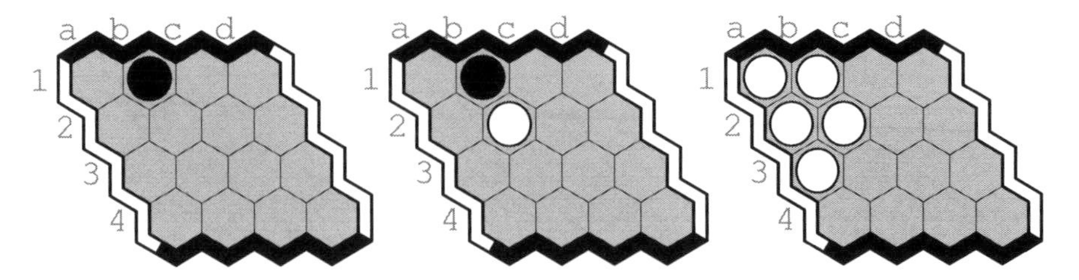

Figure 11.4. Opening, reply, equivalent position.

Assume that B has a winning strategy that opens 1.B[b1] as in Figure 11.4. After 2.W[b2] cells a2,a3 are W-captured and so can be W-filled without changing who wins. After W-filling a2 and a3, cells a1 and b1 are dead and so can be given either color without changing who wins. As in the right diagram, W-fill a1 and W-recolor b1. If B has a winning strategy with B to play in the middle diagram, B has a winning strategy with B to play in the right diagram.

Now, from the right diagram, use strategy stealing. W has cell a2 — the other four W-stones are extra and will not hurt any W-wins strategy — which is equivalent to B's initial move b1. After translating B's strategy by switching colors and edges, W steals B's strategy and wins. Both players win, contradiction. Thus 1.B[b1] is a losing opening move. This ends the proof.

That's all we know for certain for 11×11, or larger, boards: opening in each acute corner loses, and opening in each your-edge-acute-corner-neighbor loses.

This ends our introduction to Hex and math. For more on Hex, check out *Hex, The Full Story* [**24**]. That title exaggerates: the story of Hex is unfinished! Just this past year, Peter Selinger found combinatorial game theory methods that simplifiy Hex analysis, especially on boards with at most four rows [**37**], And Balodis, Ben-David, Göös, Jain and Kothari used Hex to shed light on the Alon-Saks-Seymour graph theory conjecture [**2**]. There will undoubtedly be more new Hex theorems in the coming years!

Now enjoy the last few puzzles.

11.4 puzzles

The top puzzle has seven winning moves, the others each have one. How many winning moves can you find?

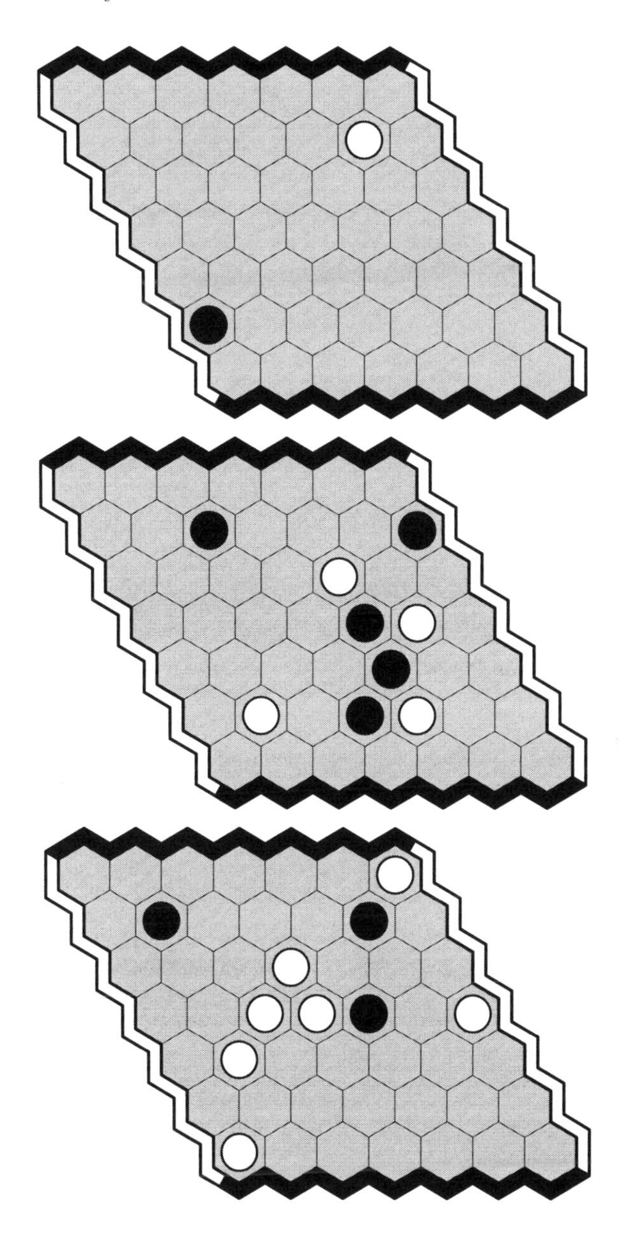

Figure 11.5. Top: B to play. Others: W to play.

11.5 solutions

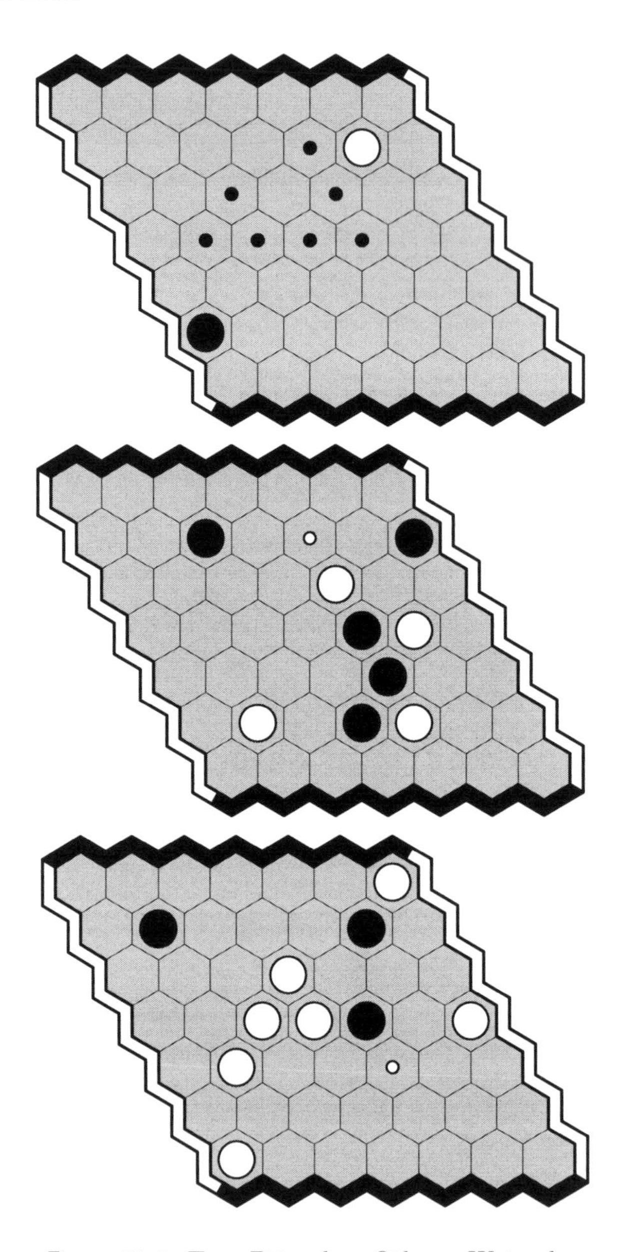

Figure 11.6. Top: B to play. Others: W to play.

12

further reading

> *This week I've been reading a lot and doing little work.*
>
> Anne Frank

this is Hex. Check out *Hex, the full story* by Hayward and Toft [**24**], a deeper look at the game and its history; *Hex Strategy: making the right connections* by Cameron Browne [**9**]; or *Connection Games* [**10**] by Browne, including many Hex-inspired games.

basics. For more on strategy, check out the interactive online *Hex: a strategy guide* by Matthew Seymour [**38**].

how Hex began. Hein's 1942-43 Polygon series in *Politiken* is the first Hex publication [**26**]. Gardner's 1957 Hex column is included in *Hexaflexagons, Probability Paradoxes, and the Tower of Hanoi* [**17, 20**]. Gardner was not convinced that Nash's discovery of Hex was independent of Hein: see *Hex, the full story* [**24**] or the Hein-Nash correspondence [**18, 25**]. You can also read about Sylvia Nasar's interviews with Nash and Gale in her Nash biography *A Beautiful Mind* [**31**].

first player wins. That Hex has no draws is equivalent to the two dimension version of Brouwer's fixed-point theorem (shown by David Gale [**15**]) or Sperner's lemma (explained by Matt DeVos and Deborah Kent in *Game Theory: a playful intro* [**12**]).

don't go there. For more on inferior cells, check out the doctoral thesis of Jack van Rijswijck [**41**] or Philip Henderson [**27**].

back to Y. Schensted and Titus designed several more games. Prompted by Irene Verona Schensted to design a game as fun as Go, they created Poly-Y, played on a board with an odd number of edges. Schensted later designed the related games Star and *Star and Titus designed Kaliko. You can read about them in *Mudcrack-Y and Poly-Y* [**36**] — available from Kadon Games — or *Connection Games* [**10**].

Robert Hochberg, Colin McDiarmid and Michael Saks used Sperner's lemma to prove a theorem that implies that Mudcrack Y — which includes regular Y and geodesic-Y as special cases — has no draws [**29**]. This together with strategy stealing implies that the first player wins.

winning strategies. Lindhard's strategy is in his archive [**30**]. Yang's report on his 7×7 strategy appeared in a computer games conference [**42**].

computers. Shannon described his Hex machine in a journal paper [**39**]. *Hex, the full story* [**24**] has a deeper discussion of computers and Hex.

uniform random Hex. Yuval Peres, Oded Schram, Scott Sheffield and David Bruce Wilson analyzed the version of random Hex in the player to move is repeatedly picked at random [**33**]. Jordan Barrett, Noah Brustle, Sarah Clusiau, Vishnu Narayan, Ndiame Ndiaye, Bruce Reed recently analyzed Hex when one player plays randomly [**3**].

dark Hex. Duane Broline gave a solution to McWorter's problem in the March 1981 edition of *Mathematics Magazine* [**8**]. For 3×4 Dark Hex where the first player's edges are four cells apart, François Bonnet showed that the first player's best mixed strategy wins with probability between .112 and .268 [**6**]. Dark Hex puzzles solutions are Nash equilibria: to learn how to find these in small problems, see DeVos and Kent [**12**]. To solve problems with thousands of possible strategies, see *Multiagent Systems* by Yoav Shoham and Kevin Leyton-Brown [**40**].

larger boards. The proofs of Beck and Holland appear in 1969 and 2000 editions of *Excursions into Mathematics* [**4, 5**]. Jakub Pawlewicz and this author's 10×10 solving algorithm is described in this paper [**32**].

Finally ... if you enjoy games and math, check out *Winning Ways for your Mathematical Plays* by Elwyn R. Berlekamp, John H. Conway, and Richard K. Guy. They passed away recently, but left behind a new branch of mathematics, combinatorial game theory. CGT even has its own undergrad textbooks, such as *Lessons in Play* by Michael H. Albert, Richard J. Nowakowski and David Wolfe or *Intro to Combinatorial Game Theory* by L.R. Haff and W.J. Garner. Aaron Siegel's *Combinatorial Game Theory* is a superb graduate-level text.

Have fun with your games and your math!

RBH, 2020

bibliography

[1] Broderick Arneson, Ryan B. Hayward, and Philip Henderson, *Solving Hex: Beyond Humans*, Computers and Games 2010 Revised Selected Papers (H.J̃aap van den Herik, Hiroyuki Iida, and Aske Plaat, eds.), Lecture Notes in Computer Science, vol. 6515, Springer, 2011, pp. 1–10.

[2] Kaspars Balodis, Shalev Ben-David, Mika Göös, Siddhartha Jain, and Robin Kothari, *Unambiguous dnfs and alon-saks-seymour*, 2021.

[3] J Barrett, N Brustle, S Clusiau, R Hayward, V Narayan, and B Reed, *Who Wins Hex When One Player Plays Randomly?*, manuscript, 2020.

[4] Anatole Beck, Michael N. Bleicher, and Donald W. Crowe, *Excursions into Mathematics*, Worth, New York, 1969, republished as [**5**].

[5] ———, *Excursions into Mathematics, Millennium Edition*, A.K. Peters, Natick, 2000.

[6] François Bonnet, *Winning strategies in darkhex: Hex with hidden stones*, Journal International Computer Games Association **40** (2018), no. 3, 234–245.

[7] Duane Broline, *Kriegspiel hex: Solution 1084*, Mathematics Magazine **54**, no. 2, 84–87.

[8] Duane Broline, *Solution to problem 1084: Kreigspiel hex*, Mathematics Magazine **54** (1981), no. 2, 85–86.

[9] Cameron Browne, *Hex Strategy: Making the Right Connections*, AK Peters, Natick, 2000.

[10] ———, *Connection Games: Variations on a Theme*, A.K. Peters, Natick, 2005.

[11] The Sage Developers, *SageMath, the Sage Mathematics Software System (v9.3)*, `https://www.sagemath.org/`, 2021.

[12] Matt DeVos and Deborah A. Kent, *Game Theory: A Playful Introduction*, AMS, 2010.

[13] Reiner Martin et al., *HexWiki*, `https://www.hexwiki.net/index.php/Main_Page`, 2005-2021.

[14] Timo Ewalds, *Morat*, `https://github.com/tewalds/morat`, 2014-2021.

[15] David Gale, *Game of Hex and the Brouwer Fixed Point Theorem*, American Math Monthly **86** (1979), no. 10, 818–827.

[16] Jacob Garber, *Geodesic-y*, `https://github.com/jwgarber/geodesic-y`, 2020-2021.

[17] Martin Gardner, *Mathematical Games: Concerning the game of Hex, which may be played on the tiles of the bathroom floor*, Scientific American **197** (1957), no. 1, 145–150.

[18] ———, *Martin Gardner Papers*, Stanford University Library, 1957-1997, Game files Hex (box 2 folder 5) and Rex (box 33 folder 5).

[19] ———, *2nd Scientific American Book of Mathematical Puzzles and Diversions*, ch. Recreational Logic, pp. 119–129, Simon and Schuster, New York, 1961, [Addendum discusses Shannon's Birdcage machine].

[20] ———, *Hexaflexagons, Probability Paradoxes, and the Tower of Hanoi*, ch. The Game of Hex, pp. 82–93, MAA, 2008.

[21] Bradley Hauer, *Evaluating opening moves in y with parallel decomposition*, https://webdocs.cs.ualberta.ca/~hayward/papers/solvingY.pdf, 2014.

[22] Ryan Hayward and Jack van Rijswijck, *Hex and Combinatorics*, Discrete Math **306** (2006), no. 19-20, 2515–2528.

[23] Ryan B. Hayward, Yngvi Björnsson, Michael Johanson, Morgan Kan, Nathan Po, and Jack van Rijswijck, *Solving 7x7 Hex: Virtual Connections and Game-state Reduction*, Advances in Computer Games (H. Jaap van den Herik, Hiroyuki Iida, and Ernst A. Heinz, eds.), vol. 263, Kluwer, Boston, 2003, pp. 261–278.

[24] Ryan B. Hayward and Bjarne Toft, *Hex, the full story*, CRC Press, 2019.

[25] Piet Hein, *Piet Hein Papers*, Archive of Anni and Hugo Hein, Middlefart, Denmark.

[26] ———, Vil De laere Polygon?, *Politiken* newspaper, page 4, December 26 1942.

[27] Philip Henderson, *Playing and Solving Hex*, Ph.D. thesis, University of Alberta, Edmonton, Alberta, Canada, Fall 2010, https://webdocs.cs.ualberta.ca/~hayward/theses/ph.pdf.

[28] Jim Hicks, *A Poet with a Slide Rule: Piet Hein Bestrides Art and Science*, Life Magazine **61** (1966), no. 16, 55–66.

[29] R. Hochberg, C. McDiarmid, and M. Saks, *On the bandwidth of triangulated triangles*, Discrete Math (1995), 261–265.

[30] Jens Lindhard, *The Jens Lindhard Papers*, History of Science Archives, Center for Science Studies, Aarhus University, Denmark.

[31] Sylvia Nasar, *A Beautiful Mind*, Touchstone, New York, 1998.

[32] Jakub Pawlewicz and Ryan B. Hayward, *Scalable Parallel DFPN Search*, Computers and Games 2013 Revised Selected Papers, Lecture Notes in Computer Science, vol. 8427, Springer, 2014, pp. 138–150.

[33] Yuval Peres, Oded Schramm, Scott Sheffield, and David Bruce Wilson, *Random-turn hex and other selection games*, The American Mathematical Monthly **114** (2007), no. 5, 373–387.

[34] John R. Pierce, *Symbols, Signals and Noise*, pp. 10–13, Harper and Brothers, 1961.

[35] Stefan Reisch, *Hex ist PSPACE-vollständig*, Acta Informatica **15** (1981), 167–191.

[36] Craige Schensted and Charles Titus, *Mudcrack Y and Poly-Y*, Neo Press, Peaks Island, Maine, 1975.

[37] Peter Selinger, *On the combinatorial value of hex positions*, 2021.

[38] Matthew Seymour, *Hex: a strategy guide*, http://www.mseymour.ca/hex_book/hexstrat.html, 2020.

[39] Claude E. Shannon, *Computers and Automata*, Proc. Inst. Radio Engineers **41** (1953), 1234–1241.

[40] Yoav Shoham and Kevin Leyton-Brown, *Multiagent Systems: Algorithmic, Game Theoretic, and Logical Foundations*, Cambridge UP, 2009.

[41] Jack van Rijswijck, *Set Colouring Games*, Ph.D. thesis, University of Alberta, Edmonton, Alberta, Canada, Fall 2006, https://webdocs.cs.ualberta.ca/~hayward/theses/ph.pdf.

[42] Jing Yang, Simon Liao, and Mirek Pawlak, *On a decomposition method for finding winning strategy in Hex game*, Proc. 1st Intl. Conf. Appl. and Devt. 21st Century Computer Games ADCOG 2001, 2001, pp. 96–111.

index of names

index

THE JOY OF KNOWING

The Joy of Knowing Pete

Much was said, yet no words spoken

Hazel Morgan

YOUCAXTON
PUBLICATIONS

ISBN 978-1-914424-52-6
Published by YouCaxton Publications 2022
YCBN: 01

YouCaxton Publications
www.youcaxton.co.uk

Layout and typography: Ella Knight

Font: Garamond Premier Pro 12pt

To Andy and Philip, in gratitude for all we shared
in the eighteen years of Peter's life.

Acknowledgements

AS I LOOK back, I want to give my heartfelt thanks to all Peter's friends, to pupils and staff at Riverwalk and Belstead Schools, to those who provided short breaks, to those in clubs he belonged to and all those in the church who cared for him, especially the late Canon Richard Norburn. They are all part of Peter's story. We have treasured the memories our friends shared with us, some written down for us to keep.

I am grateful that we lived in the grounds of Culford School where we were part of the community and where Peter had some good friends among staff and pupils. Indeed, we remain indebted to Deirdre who regularly puts flowers on his grave.

Our families were generous in their support, especially my mother who would do anything she could to help us and Peter.

I recall with gratitude the times we spent in North Yorkshire where we could relax and recharge our batteries.

Without the provision of care in the Chantry, the Sue Ryder home, the last months of Peter's life could have been very different and I am so glad to recognise the contribution of staff, residents and the chaplain, Revd. Peter Gibbs.

My colleagues at the Mental Health Foundation, the self-advocates and family carers, the professionals I met through my work all taught me so much and helped to give me a broader perspective which I hope is reflected in this book. Now my friends at People First Dorset reinforce my belief in the importance of community and friendship; a big thank you to them.

The writers, Sally Bayley and Virginia Astley provided invaluable advice in the later stages of writing on style and structure. I am indebted to them. I am grateful to Laura Kerr for her encouragement, Emma Hawker for preparing the photos and to Catriona Duncan and Ruth Bettenson for proof reading. I have appreciated the support of Bob Fowke at YouCaxton and Liz Gordon at Brilliant Fish.

Thank you to our son, Philip for his suggestions. For him it was a bittersweet read.

Above all I am so grateful to my husband, Andy, who has listened to me talking endlessly about the book, patiently heard my concerns and read it several times in different versions. For him it was also a hard read and I really appreciated his suggestions and above all his love and support.

Foreword

I HAVE KNOWN Hazel Morgan for over twenty years. Time seems to fly past so quickly! I first met her when she was working for the Foundation for People with Learning Disabilities in London. We were fortunate enough to be given a grant to begin an exploration into the spiritual needs of people living with learning disabilities. I was the researcher and Hazel oversaw and managed the research. I enjoyed that project very much. The Foundation was fully committed to the idea and Hazel was a great person to be managing the project. As I got to know her, I discovered her passion. She was someone who was wholly committed to enhancing the lives of people with learning disabilities. It was clear from the start that hers was not just a professional interest. I knew from the piercing questions she would ask of the research, and the vital editorial suggestions that she made along the way that this was someone who knew what she was talking about and knew where the needs lay. In the end, I think we produced some good work and hopefully people will have benefitted from it over the years.

I can't remember when, but at some point along the way I read Hazel's book *Through Peter's Eyes.* It was and remains a deep, moving and personal reflection on her son Peter, who lived with Down's syndrome, and the wonderful impact that he had on her and her family and friends. As I read that book, I began to understand the roots of Hazel's passion. She not only understood the issues, she had also lived them. As I came to understand Peter through Hazel's words, I began to understand her passion in the work that we did then and continued to do for a number of years.

Hazel clearly learned a lot from Peter. And that learning continues in this book, as Hazel, thoughtfully, carefully, sometimes poetically, captures fresh dimensions of Peter's life and allows all of us access to the wisdom that Peter brought to her life.

This is a lovely book. It's a testimony to Peter, but it is much more than that. It's a gentle and thoughtful counter to the way the world is. In a world that assumes there is nothing to be learned from people with learning disabilities, Hazel gently and kindly brings Peter's voice to the fore and helps us to see just how wrong such a view is. If you take the time to dwell in the story, you will begin to see the world just a little differently.

John Swinton
Professor in Practical Theology and Pastoral Care
The University of Aberdeen

Contents

PROLOGUE

Dear Pete,

Do you remember how you hated snow? When you were a little boy in Durham, everyone would congregate on Observatory Hill to ski or toboggan. Your brother would descend on plastic sacking with great glee but when we put you on the sledge for a short run, you cried. You would not have liked the weather on the day of the funeral. The sky was grey; it snowed all morning. Several friends have told me that, as we left Culford Church, the sun broke through the trees, creating a 'winter wonderland'. I did not notice. My eyes were firmly fixed on the backs of the bearers. When we stopped at the graveside, I did look up. People were streaming along the yew-lined path. Amid all the emotions of that day, I felt proud, proud that you had touched so many lives.

Being a proud mum was not a description I would have attributed to myself before that week, associating it with those whose sons and daughters were high achievers. Yet when your teacher, Maggie, in a condolence letter, wrote, 'You must be proud of Pete', I knew that she was right. I told Philip of this discovery.

'Mum, you've always been proud of Pete. You must know that.' Looking back now, I believe I was.

In your eighteen years you led a full life despite enormous disabilities. You had Down's syndrome; infant spasms hindered your progress. You were partially hearing and could not talk. At the age of seven, you had surgery to repair a hole in your heart. You were very short sighted and allergic to gluten. Yet, although you had your frustrations, you enjoyed your life. You were gentle and affectionate but you also had great determination. I believe that this helped you to survive the very severe strokes you suffered just before the previous Christmas. When you went to the Chantry, the Sue Ryder home, after spending three months in hospital, amazingly you seemed happy, despite having had a tracheostomy and a gastrostomy and being immobile.

While you were there, your Dad and I made a collection of photos to help us chat about past events and friends, about the years in Durham until you were eight, and our life in Suffolk. Often days would pass without us bringing out the album for there was so much else to talk about from the present: your life in the home and your new friends among staff and residents.

Now I can only dwell on the past, the memories evoked by those photos, by friends we shared and by places we visited. When I described your early life in my first book, it was through your eyes.[1] Now as I focus on your teenage years, I would not presume to do this. How could I know what you, a young man, were feeling? I have to admit that I would also find it too painful to imagine your suffering during your final illness so vividly.

My memories of living with you during those years are like a kaleidoscope. They assume a pattern, which shifts and alters as new images come to my mind. At the centre was our home; beyond was the life of Dad's day and boarding school. Then there were your own schools – the one local and the other at some distance that you attended from the age of fifteen. I can picture your friends, times in the local town and countryside, scenes from our holidays. The focus changes: life became contained within hospital walls and within a Sue Ryder Home. As I look back, of course we shared your frustrations and, in the final months, your suffering, but there was also intensity,

1 Hazel Morgan Through Peter's Eyes (Arthur James 1990)

joy, colour and light. It has been strange, Pete, that Dad and I had the independent thought that although your life was short, it was in so many ways complete. Your greatest gift to me, and I believe to many of those around you, was to teach us the meaning of living in the moment and of love. That is your legacy, and no one could wish for a better.

Ten years later, surrounded by a group of friends, we planted a redwood sapling in your memory close to the bungalow where we had all lived together and where Dad and I had remained until we moved into the town a few months before we retired. I said a few words and Philip spoke:

> 'I would like to share some of my memories of Pete with you:
> Pete running on tiptoe, arms swinging back;
> His love of music;
> The fourteen Vivaldi videos;
> The wind-up "row, row, row your boat" held up to his ear;
> His home-made cassettes of piano playing with his added vocal parts;
> Him putting his head through the windows to hear the bells in Durham;
> His happy noises, his grumbling noises;
> His abilities of persuasion; getting his plate or his coat or waving goodbye;
> His Primula cheese spread, gluten-free bread, crisps, rides in the car.
> How did he bounce up and down on his bed using his ankles?
> His frustration, banging his head and scratching;
> Him putting his hair back on his head when he had had it cut;

> His catalogue he would like to pat;
> His smile and ability to engage and charm those around him.
> As Pete did not have words, I don't think there are words to describe his special
> qualities, that managed to have such an impact on people around him, and are
> evident from you all being here today.
> I would like to thank you for coming. I would also like to thank Mum and Dad
> for organising this tree so Pete's memory has a living representation of how
> Pete continues to influence our lives.'

Now your name is mentioned on a website: 'The impressive building that is Culford School is complemented by a magnificent row of Giant Redwoods. One has been reduced to a stump and one has had to be cut part of the way down, but the rest are in superb condition. A pleasant surprise was finding three young Wellingtonia, one with a plaque that reads 'In loving memory of Peter Morgan (1977 - 1995) who so enjoyed living in Culford Park''.[2]

---

2 Redwood World http://www.redwoodworld.co.uk/ See under captions and pictures, listings under Suffolk, Culford.

CHAPTER 1

'Poor Pete, he can't have an adventure on his own.'

ONE DAY, PETER saw the front door open and decided on an adventure. He headed out across the grass and turned down the drive towards the Iron Gates. He wasn't setting out up the road, past the village church on the left and towards Culford Hall and the school buildings, where his dad, Andy, was deputy head and where his brother and some of Pete's own friends were pupils. He certainly wasn't wanting a country walk in the school grounds, going towards the trees, by the ha-ha onto the path to the river, nor did he wish to explore behind our home and across the playing fields. He was intent on going into the village.

'Quick, Andy! Can you catch Pete? He's off on his own down the road!' Fortunately, we witnessed him setting out. We could see a sturdy figure walking typically on tiptoe, jauntily swinging his arms in unison backwards and forwards.

'Pete, what are you doing?' Andy called, racing after him.

Pete walked on determinedly, undeterred. Andy decided it was best to walk alongside him. Fortunately, then there was little traffic on that route but on the other side of the gates was a busy road.

We knew well that his goal was the house of his friend Deirdre, the wife of one of Andy's colleagues. She invited us to Sunday lunch once a term. This was Pete's favourite: meat, roast potatoes, and several vegetables with a delicious pudding such as a pavlova to follow. He seemed to imagine that if he landed on her doorstep, such a meal would be placed in front of him automatically.

'Bring the car round,' Andy called to me as he dashed off and so I set out for Deirdre's road, ready to pick up Andy and Pete, as a ride in the car would usually distract him.

It hadn't been our plan to go out that morning but having persuaded Pete to get in his usual back seat, we set out, music blaring *Bridge over Troubled Waters*, a favourite of both Andy and Pete. We drove through Thetford Forest, a circular trip which diverted him.

Later that day when his brother came home, we recounted the story to him.

'Poor Pete, he can't have adventures on his own. He always has to have someone with him,' responded Philip.

Philip was able to go out into the four hundred acres of the school grounds with his friend Paul, whose father was also a teacher, especially when they were both around in the school holidays. Paul would call at the front door and the two of them would set out with nothing but instructions to be back at lunchtime. On his return Philip would call 'Hi Pete' and give him a high five. Pete would grin. What did Pete think as his brother disappeared for several hours? He was more confined to his home in a quiet part of the school grounds and spent more time with his parents, especially me.

Philip was right. Pete influenced our lives profoundly. Through him we learnt so much. After he died, how could I continue to teach history part-time in college and university when I had learnt so much from him? I felt I had to find a job where I could work with people with learning disabilities and their families. I saw an advert for a Learning Disabilities Manager at the Mental Health Foundation (MHF) and responded. I had nothing to lose. For ten years I made the long journey into London as we built up the Foundation for People with Learning Disabilities within the MHF. We carried out research and projects to improve people's lives. I could work on the train alongside the commuters. I had a choice: the route on the Norwich line seemed more convivial than the shorter journey via Cambridge. One day a young man was on the phone reporting at some length that his wife had given birth concluding by announcing 'and then the baby just popped out!'. The carriage burst into applause. In contrast the travellers on the Cambridge line were more serious. When a man was speaking loudly on a long and confidential business call a young woman went up the aisle, crouched by him and sang an aria loudly in his ear. The rest of us looked down at our papers and pretended nothing out of the ordinary was happening. From the hurly burly of London, I would return to the quiet bungalow within the grounds of Culford School. We were surrounded by our vivid memories with time to reflect.

CHAPTER TWO

'As I wandered through the rooms, memories constantly pierced me.'

IN MANY RESPECTS the tied home in the grounds of his father's school was ideal for Peter. It was on one level with a spacious living room and kitchen at one end and bedrooms and bathrooms off a passage. There was no danger of him clambering on a radiator and pulling down the sash window to get closer to the cathedral bells as had happened while in Durham. We moved to Suffolk when Pete was eight and so he lived there for almost a decade until his final illness. This was his home in term time and for parts of the holidays. When we could, we went to our own home near the coast in North Yorkshire but, for the greater part of the year, the school bungalow was the centre of his life. I certainly believe he felt secure there. Place was always important to him.

People talk about the quietness when their sons or daughters leave home, but there was nothing like the long silence as we continued to live in the bungalow. As I wandered through the rooms, memories constantly pierced me. I wonder if the kitchen was Pete's favourite: I remembered how the weekdays began there. Once he went to school in Ipswich at the age of fifteen, he had to be ready for the taxi at 7.45. We used to follow a strict regime. We woke him about 7.15 and he had breakfast in his pyjamas. Although still half asleep, he was always good-tempered. At the table, I sat opposite and Andy beside him. That was unless he decided otherwise. Sometimes Pete moved the chair to the end of the table, as much as to say, 'I think I'll be independent today'. That usually happened at more leisurely meals. One day he put the pot of marmalade on the floor and grinned, looking round the table at us. On school days there was no time for such jokes. At 7.35, we knew he had to get dressed. He helped by putting his arms through his sleeves and pulling up his trousers.

Having waited up the road, perhaps thinking he was out of our sight, at 7.45 on the dot, Jim drew up on the drive. He faithfully drove over from his home in Felixstowe to take Pete to and from school in his taxi each day. I can still hear him on the doorstep saying, 'All aboard', and then once he was in the car, 'No, Pete, don't take your boots off'. Pete had phases of removing his boots in all sorts of unlikely places. We felt it was an indication that he was comfortable. Jim played music on the way to school. Carole and later Brenda were his morning escorts who sat quietly beside him. They were good friends to him. On the way they picked up little Naomi, who also went to a special school in Ipswich. She used to like to sing to Pete on the journey. I wonder what she sang? I can imagine him moving, vocalising and smiling in the back of the car.

After Pete had departed, Philip would get ready to go to school just up the road, Andy would disappear for his busy day as a deputy head, and I would tidy up and prepare for whatever hours of teaching I might have in local colleges. My timetable would vary from year to year.

When Pete returned from school, I used to give Jim and Neil, the afternoon escort, a drink before their long return journey. Pete would take himself off to look in the kitchen to see if I was likely to prepare a snack. He might return to the hall and grab my sleeve. Sometimes he would wave vigorously at Jim and Neil.

'So, you want us to go, Pete?'

'Oh Pete, don't be so rude,' I would say and Jim would smile.

Pete was even known to have gone to the fridge and arranged cold ham and beans on a plate for himself before they departed. Food was important to him. He certainly thought that things should be properly served and that he should sit down at the table. He also thought that a main meal comprised meat or fish and two vegetables. We heard that he created a drama at school when the meal was macaroni cheese. I guess he would have pushed it away, making his grumbling noises. We'd learnt that it was not a good idea to give him a vegetarian meal!

At the weekend, on Saturdays Pete thought that he shouldn't get dressed and loved to be around the house in his pyjamas. Admittedly they were very smart, rather like a jogging suit, because it was no use buying ones with buttons, which would pop off if he tried to get out of his top. Pete and I used to get up late, after Andy and Philip had gone to school. We listened to music, watched videos and played with the keyboard. With all this musical entertainment woe betide me if I said, 'It's time to get dressed, Pete.'

He firmly pulled down his top. He might make his protesting sounds. Was it worth making an issue? Andy pretended to be shocked to find he was still in his pyjamas when he returned about midday.

'Aren't you dressed yet, Pete?'

If we needed to go out during the morning, I put on my outdoor coat to indicate what was going to happen and Pete accepted, if reluctantly, that possibly something exciting was going to occur and with my assistance got dressed.

The large living room was the other centre of our home and family life. Pete was always pleased if I began to lay the table in the dining room end, rather than in the kitchen, as he knew there would be a special meal. He would scrutinise the blue table mats with their pictures of sailing boats as he waited. Once the meal started, he would glance over his shoulder at the sideboard to make sure that there was a pudding, not the usual yoghurt and ice cream.

In later years when I looked, I could see a small burn mark on the table. It happened when we were celebrating Pete's sixteenth birthday with Jo, Wendy and Fiona, his friends from Andy's school who used to visit him weekly. Pete had met Wendy as her mother ran a monthly club on a Saturday for youngsters with learning disabilities that he attended. She was sometimes a helper. I had laid tea for four so that he could entertain them on his own.

'Oh, Pete, you can't want to eat any more.' I could overhear Fiona from the kitchen.

When Andy and Philip returned from school, we brought in the cake and sang *Happy Birthday* not very tunefully. Pete smiled to himself, his eyes transfixed by the candles. The girls helped him to blow them out.

We cleared the table for indoor fireworks. Pete particularly liked the golden cascades. His face would light up and he would tense in excitement. When we had the sparklers, we all wanted to entertain him and made patterns in the air. Unthinkingly we held them too close to the table. Clearing up later, we found the burn. I was glad it was there even though the table had just been polished by a furniture restorer. It reminded me of a happy time with Pete surrounded by his friends.

Although Pete often welcomed meals in the dining area of our living room as they would be special, sometimes it was a different story. If strangers arrived, he could be reluctant to sit up and would eye them suspiciously. He liked the familiar or those who he felt related to him. He seemed to have an innate sense of those who connected with him and did not ignore him. Maybe he also felt that my attention would be diverted.

Nonetheless, in his mind, the living room was the place where we and he entertained. Regularly our vicar, Richard, made pastoral visits to see him at home. 'Shall we say a prayer?' he would say when Pete appeared likely to be attentive. One day he arrived when Pete was looking at his catalogues in his bedroom. He went to join him, but Pete took him firmly by the hand and led him to the sitting room. Like everyone else, Richard had his proper place.

An alternative place to entertain in the summer was on the grass at the front of the bungalow. We might have a barbecue. We would arrange picnic chairs and a table outside. Andy and Philip would get the barbecue out of the garage and light the charcoal. On these occasions Pete would be unusually patient. He seemed to appreciate it took time to cook the meal. It was a chance for all of us to relax while the sun was setting behind the church a little way up the road, casting its rays over the conifers and the myriad of trees beyond. Sometimes we might invite friends.

In Pete's early teens, when he was still at school locally, we invited his class for a barbecue lunch in the summer term. They were all expected mid-morning and I could not get the barbecue to light. Pete's friend Daniel, who lived in the village and occasionally sat in with him, was helping. He came to my rescue. Arriving early, he went off to the garage to buy some firelighters. We then had the opposite problem and had to douse the flames! Luckily, when everyone arrived, the meal was well underway. They all sat round except Pete's friend Russell who, I remember, took himself off and was trying to get into one of the cars. He loved sitting in a driving seat and had to be guided away. The rain stayed off long enough for us to eat the meal outside and then we had to take refuge indoors. After Pete became ill, we didn't have the heart for a barbecue.

Pete's day would always finish with a leisurely bath. I had almost forgotten how he loved to linger in the warm water. He explored the bubbles, touching them, holding them up and peering at them clustered in his hand. Sometimes he examined his bath book. It was my friend, Katie, a mum whom I had met through Peter's local school, who jolted my memory. She described how her son David loved his bath.

'Did you have trouble getting Pete out of the bath?'

'Oh, no.'

'We sometimes have to put on the cold tap.'

'Of course, we did! I remember now. We used to say "cold-water treatment, Pete". He used to grin and stand up quickly, grabbing the towel rail for support as he stepped out. We would wrap a towel round him and guide him to his room.'

CHAPTER THREE

'I can picture him now sitting on Philip's bed ... as his brother played the Irish drum.'

AS I WALKED along the passage in our silent bungalow, I could look into Philip's room at the back, prepared for his visits home; he was working in London. We kept Pete's room opposite as it had been, while putting out some cherished objects on the shelves: his wooden jigsaw of the letters of his name, his christening mug, the mould of his foot he had made at school.

It had always been simply furnished, just a bed, an inbuilt cupboard and a chest of drawers, which sometimes he tipped over. I recalled how he loved trampolining at school and decided to practise at home. One bed collapsed and then another. He must have enjoyed the motion and the rhythm. In the end we acquired a discarded iron bedstead from Andy's school. He could bounce to his heart's content. When he was in his early teens, he used to like to spend time in his room listening to music. He waved to us, which was his way of telling us to leave, and then came to find us and grabbed our hands when the tape was finished.

He used to love going in to see Philip in his room, although he wasn't very impressed during Philip's heavy-metal phase. He liked a melody, preferring his brother's Irish folk music with its tunes and rhythms, and I can picture him now sitting on Philip's bed with a wide grin on his face, as his brother played the Irish drum. At one stage, we made a 'boys' room' from the spare room and put in an old sofa, TV and video recorder.

Pete had favourite pieces of music but after a while his preferences would shift. He had a phase when he loved the Big Band sound: he particularly liked *In the Mood*. He would take my hand to start it again. Then he preferred *Mack the Knife*. Next there was the video of Young Musician of the Year. He loved Nicola Loud playing Bruch's *Violin Concerto*. He would sit enthralled, tensing in enjoyment, taking my hand to put it on again and again. When today I hear these strong melodies that he so enjoyed, it is as if a blade is twisting deep within. I had the chance to go and hear this concerto with my granddaughter and her mum recently and I declined as I wasn't sure I would cope. The next favourite was Nigel Kennedy playing Vivaldi's *Four Seasons*. Three tapes became worn out and had to be thrown away. If we tried to introduce another, he turned it off. Despite his hearing loss, it was as if his innate musical sense was very acute.

We used to joke that if the Pied Piper of Hamelin arrived, Pete would be at the head of the queue. When he was a small boy, and we were living in Durham we would go to the brass-band concert in the park on a Sunday afternoon. It was wonderful until they took a break. Then Pete set off quickly towards the musicians. He rushed to pick up a trumpet. Fortunately, by chance it belonged to the husband of his reception-class teacher who was not put out by this. As well as the heavy metal he chose to ignore, he was not so tolerant of beginners. I recall him trying to remove the saxophone from an inexperienced player who wanted to entertain him.

Did he inherit my grandmother's innate musicality? For us it was a real gift that he gained such enjoyment from melodies. So many sounds reverberated round our home in those days. Alongside Pete's music we might hear the sounds of his brother's band from the garage, with Philip on the drums and his friends on guitars.

When Peter was just sixteen, he indicated forcibly that he didn't wish to be on his own at bedtime and would firmly shut the door to stop us leaving. He became very agitated and often banged his head on the bedroom carpet. It was very hard to cope when he hurt himself. We went to talk to the new clinical psychologist, Chris, after school and he made sure that he included Pete in the conversation. Pete responded by sitting quietly. He became restless if he was ignored. There were occasions when people talked about Pete as if he wasn't there and wouldn't try to draw him in.

We kept a diary of Pete's behaviour. We discovered that he was likely to become upset if constipated. A regular mild laxative helped, but he still disliked being by himself and the parting at night. We tried to ensure that there was a well-established routine – a bath, a quiet social time and bed – but even that did not always help. We would take him into our bed and give him a cuddle to reassure him. At last, he'd settle in his room. At our few meetings Chris expressed the view that this distress was linked to Philip's departure to university several months before. I am sure this was so. It was difficult to explain why the brother who had been his companion and a constant presence in his life disappeared for weeks on end.

We made the boys' room into a spare bedroom once more as Pete wouldn't want to be in there on his own and we put the video recorder in the sitting room. I can picture him sitting on the floor, his ear close to the television. By this time a recording of the 1990 Tchaikovsky music competition, a mixture of performances and interviews had become the favourite. At one stage, an interview was interrupted by a drunk shouting in Russian and the wife of the eventual winner said, 'It is very rude'. Pete thought this was hilarious. We always wondered how much he understood. He loved the rendering of Rachmaninov's *Third Piano Concerto*. Was it the strong melodies that excited him causing him to become taut in enjoyment and anticipation?

He certainly had the best taste in music in our house. Sometimes we would bring out the keyboard and he would love to listen to Brahms' *Lullaby* again and again.

He always pulled a coffee table in front of him and would spread out big catalogues around him. He would select one and turn the pages with a resounding thump. He seemed to find this very satisfying. He would collect a packet of crisps, salt and vinegar preferably, a slice of gluten-free bread with cheese spread, and special biscuits. These he would pile up like bricks. He didn't necessarily eat them; it was as if he needed the comfort of knowing they were there and revelled in the pattern and the arrangement. I used to worry that he was having too many snacks. Later in the evening we'd say the kitchen was closed and tie up the door.

Another favourite musical offering was the tape made by his musician friend, Margaret. I can picture him close to his tape recorder. I look back on our first meeting with her. She accompanied Howard, a peripatetic music teacher from the school to our house. He came to see how they could help Peter musically as he had had music therapy in Durham. Howard, who had played with Benny Goodman in the thirties, brought out several saxophones. Pete was very excited. He smiled broadly. Margaret accompanied on the keyboard. We gladly accepted her offer to come to our house regularly. When she arrived, Pete would take her to the piano and balance himself on her knee. He would place his hands on hers and she would play, so they raced over the keys playing melodies 'together'.

'Poor Margaret', we would say, 'you're getting such a big boy!'

Was that a highlight of his week?

When we planted the wellingtonia in his memory, after we had moved away, and looked at the exterior of the bungalow, it felt familiar yet unfamiliar, evoking so many memories. Even if Pete would have preferred to have been closer to the action, watching comings and goings at the school, Andy and I were happy that our home stood alone about a hundred yards from the church in a quiet area of the grounds. We couldn't disturb others with Pete's constant music, not to mention the sound of Philip's drums.

CHAPTER FOUR

'I can see him now, grown up into a strapping lad, walking past our cottage, perhaps going up to watch the rugby with Dad.'

WHEN WE FIRST retired, we lived for ten years, four miles away from Culford in the centre of Bury St Edmunds in a late medieval house. With its beams and inglenook fireplace, a front door onto a narrow lane and with adjoining neighbours, it was a great contrast to our home at the school, yet it also felt warm and welcoming. We would return regularly to Culford to put flowers on Peter's grave, to go to functions at the school and for walks in the extensive grounds. On each occasion, memories of our life with Peter hit us.

When we visited to put flowers on his grave, we drove through the Iron Gates of the estate, which had previously belonged to the Cadogan family and had been sold to the school in 1935. We parked alongside the hedge in front of the graveyard and looked back at our bungalow now with unfamiliar cars in front of the garage. If we lingered, so many pictures came to mind. In the summer Pete sometimes went off with Fiona, Jo and Wendy, the three pupils who came to spend time with him each week. In good weather, they would have a picnic under the trees nearby. Pete was always happy to accompany them, and I could hear his chuckles as the girls chatted to him. In front of the church are the gnarled yews whose sturdy branches splayed horizontally which later made an exciting climbing frame for our young nephew and nieces. How Pete would have loved watching them.

Looking across to the flint church, we could recall how one year he enjoyed the informal candle-lit carol service so close to where we had lived. Traditionally the pupils dressed up. Pete did not but he sat quietly, fascinated by the flames, caught up in the music. The next year, I stayed at home, and he went with Andy. I was fondly imagining how much he would be enjoying the service when the key turned in the lock.

'Pete was very restless and wouldn't sit still and be quiet,' Andy explained.

It was the only way he could tell us he didn't wish to be there or perhaps preferred to be at home.

Opposite the church are the semi-detached Victorian flint cottages; the nearest one was the home of the school gardener and his wife. They were our closest neighbours. During Peter's lifetime, Mr. and Mrs. Langley lived there. Affectionately we recalled how Gordon Langley was so proud of being from Norfolk. He always told Philip, 'You don't want to grow up to be a gardener, boy. You want to be an academic.'

Tricia, his wife, was friendly and kind. We could call on them in a crisis. I remember looking for Gordon to help me catch a bird that had flown into the sitting room. It turned out that they had many memories of Pete. Tricia wrote after Pete died: 'I can see Pete now, sitting in his buggy with Mum and Dad out for a stroll, pointing things out to him.'

She remembered when he went to the local school: 'I can see the mini-bus calling for him... in the morning and then returning in the afternoon, with Mum or Dad waiting on the porch to welcome him home. The day we had a power cut I took some batteries down to the bungalow for Pete's radio, just as the minibus returned. Mum was on the porch with Peter's radio in her hand and he could not get there quick enough to take it from her, to listen to his music.'

Tricia continued, 'I can see him now, grown up into a strapping lad, walking past our cottage, perhaps going up to watch the rugby with Dad.'

Walking further up the road I could see the school swimming pool, to our right. What memories that evoked! When it was newly built, Pete was one of the most enthusiastic members of the sports club. I can picture him now, handing his ticket to Derek or Glen at the reception, disappearing into the changing rooms with Andy. He emerged first on to the poolside, arm bands on, walking fast along the edge. I hovered, fearful lest he might fall, but he always seemed sure-footed. Then Andy appeared and we would help Pete into the water and guide him towards the deep end. He made the water swirl around him. He didn't bother to swim unless he was out of his depth. Andy used to hold him until his feet no longer touched the bottom and then he'd let go and gently push Pete away. Andy encouraged him to swim the width of the pool, pretending they were having a race. With a grin, Pete often circled back and grabbed Andy.

'No, Pete, you can swim.'

After a while we let him potter round in the shallow end to his heart's content.

The new swimming pool also created problems. Pete decided he no longer wished to go for a walk and would head for the sports centre instead. He didn't understand, or didn't wish to understand, that he could only go at certain allocated times. I can remember that one day I had to call to someone who was passing to fetch Andy from the school to help me. Pete sat down at the turning to the sports centre and refused to move. On another occasion he dashed for the main door. That time, Andy was with us and so I went home to collect the car as nothing else would have induced him to leave except the prospect of a ride. Then we had a reverse problem. He suddenly decided that going swimming no longer held the same attractions, refused to go in and headed off round the side of the building. Sometimes when we were on the hockey fields near the village street, he would decide to visit Deirdre in the hopes of finding a Sunday roast lunch.

If we go to the South Front, the gardens behind Culford Hall, which is the main school building, as we might when visiting on an Open Day, I can imagine the annual Charity Fair each September. Stalls and sideshows were scattered about the quiet and formal gardens. The younger pupils dashed from one to the other, hair wet from bobbing apples, faces white from searching for sweets in flour-filled bowls. One year, Pete was intrigued to see Philip and Andy sitting astride a horizontal pole, beating each other with feather pillows, trying to dislodge the other. I can't remember who won. He preferred to watch and would sit up at a table with a packet of crisps and his favourite blackcurrant drink. On another occasion he was close to his friend Fiona's stall. He was happy amid the noise and excitement.

However, if we walk up past the north front with its imposing porch and eighteenth century façade, we might recall how once a year Andy would set out to push Peter round the half marathon course, until we decided the major buggy must be abandoned and he should walk as much as possible. After that, it was no longer practical for him to join in the charity race. Instead, we took a picnic up to the finish and sat on a rug beside the track to watch the runners as they came across the finishing line. He accompanied Andy into the tuck shop to buy some crisps and a carton of drink. He liked being part of the school life, but he often adopted a spectator's role.

Occasionally, we would go into the main building. He would make a range of noises, enjoying the echoes when we paused in the Old Hall or by the wide staircase. I remember a brass band concert in the larger modern main hall which had been incorporated into the building. The performers, some Cambridge students, appreciated his involvement, even if it meant some vocalising along with them. We tried to keep him on his chair, but he really preferred to sit on the floor. Andy would sometimes take him to rehearsals for the school musicals. Gillian, the producer and one of Pete's friends recalls his gift of 'spontaneous joy'.

One of Pete's favourite events was the charity restaurant, run by the pupils before Christmas. We sat at tables in the imposing staff room in the main building. The log fire blazed. Sometimes we joined a large group of friends. After the meal Pete went in search of the yellow pages on the telephone table in the corner. I never understood why he liked large books so much. He would pat them and turn the pages. It must have been satisfying for him. Once we went with another family, and Pete, Luke and Nathan pulled the crackers that we took along. Sometimes we were on our own. One of our last family outings before Pete's illness was to the charity restaurant. We planned to go on the Monday with a group from church but Pete appeared to be really poorly. On the Thursday he seemed to have recovered and we booked a table for three. He sat there happily enjoying the meal. Several friends greeted us. We never dreamed that such good times were coming to an end.

Our frequent visits to the school, particularly to put flowers on Pete's grave, ended seven years ago when we moved to Dorset. I am sure he would have been happy for us to have moved near Philip and his family, nonetheless it was hard to leave him although it was made easier by his friend Deirdre offering to put flowers on his grave. As Andy is still president of the school cricket club we return at least once a year as the President's Eleven plays the school each summer. We spend most of the day by the cricket ground beyond the main hall with its thatched pavilion and river to the south. We can look back on many hours spent by the pitch with Peter. He sat on a rug with his catalogue or picnic close to the pavilion looking up at the game from time to time, Sometimes he became more interested and would focus intently as the bowler released the ball.

'Come on, Pete, let's go for a walk.'

Pete would take Andy's arm to circle the pitch, down towards the river, and on past the score box.

As he was not keen on long walks, we have fewer memories of the far-flung corners of the park beyond the cricket ground. There is however one remote spot that reminds us vividly of him. Tucked away the other side of the Iron Bridge is a clearing in the trees. The logs are scattered around. Each May, on Wesley Day (Culford being a Methodist school) about one hundred children gathered there for a campfire, barbecue and service. We sat down and Pete made excited noises.

'Shush, Pete.'

He didn't take any notice of us. He was happy to be there. The cooking was underway and sweet-smelling smoke wafted round us. When the food was served, he went and sat with a group of children and dissociated himself from us.

On our now infrequent visits, the first place we stop is the churchyard close to the bungalow. I remember Pete sitting on the bench by the wall as occasionally he might. I look at the geraniums, and sweet williams, or imagine the daffodils, polyanthus, cyclamen, pansies and other plants that Deirdre puts on his grave according to the season.

If I look across the hedge to the road, a different image comes to mind. When Pete was older and Philip had passed his driving test, Philip would take Pete for a ride in our old Vauxhall Cavalier round the countryside. In great style, they would accelerate away fast from our home and past the church, Pete characteristically flicking his glasses. Did he appreciate the feeling of being boys together and going at greater speed than usual into the wider world? He had a life outside the school gates too. We had needed variety and I guess Peter did too.

CHAPTER FIVE

'One of the homeless men who sat on the benches outside Moyse's Hall rushed up holding out a pound coin, "Please give your son this".'

WHEN WE LIVED in Bury St Edmunds after we initially retired and now when we return to the school at least once a year, driving along familiar roads, I can picture us going out with Pete in the little red Peugeot, a Motability car, to so many destinations locally and far afield, the radio or tapes blaring. Sometimes it would feel as if the car was going over an uneven road surface. We would look around and see Pete bouncing up and down in the back. He would love to remove his seat belt if he could but was quite hypocritical about this. One day, Andy took him to Cambridge station to meet a friend, who remembers how Pete lent across and tapped him on the shoulder to remind him that he hadn't fixed the belt.

Closer to home, Pete loved the bustle and busyness of the town. We did not venture with him into the medieval grid where we later lived as its quaint old houses held little interest for him. Supermarkets hold very few memories. We tried to get him involved in shopping. We thought we were doing well as he walked confidently through the greengrocery section then, when we reached the salad counter, he grabbed a spoon to help himself. We managed to retrieve it just before it reached his mouth. We did not repeat that experiment.

Pete liked the coffee room in the library. As we went up in the lift, did he anticipate sitting at the table with lemonade and crisps, lingering and looking at the people?

He always enjoyed lights and sounds. One Christmas in the market square, he was walking along, holding Andy's arm and admiring the lights. One of the homeless men who sat on the benches outside Moyse's Hall rushed up from behind us holding out a pound coin,

'Please give your son this.'

We thanked him warmly and bought some bubble bath to put under the Christmas tree. On this occasion Philip was not with us but it reminds me of the time when Peter was a very small boy and the four of us had been to the Miners' Gala in Durham. As we returned home, an old man emerging from a pub gave us money for Pete. Philip was not included in this generous gesture. Somehow Pete's vulnerability touched people and we could only say 'thank you'.

The Abbey Gardens, close to our home, was another place we would visit with Pete on summer evenings. We would walk down the long path, past the immaculate flower beds, to the swings. He particularly liked the roundabout and would stay on as long as we would push. There would not be many children around at that time. Some would sit on the roundabout with him and look with interest at the large boy sharing their pleasure. Sometimes parents would look at him suspiciously and whisk their children away. I would wonder if that hurt him as much as it hurt us? Was he bewildered by their stares and hurried withdrawal? We were beginning to think that Pete was getting too old to go to the park. Much later, they installed a large swing for people in wheelchairs. Has this made people more accepting of those with a disability?

To create some variation in the long winter evenings, I remember how we would drive into the town on some pretext, such as taking the bottles to the bottle bank. We were looking forward to the time when we would be able to take him into a pub. We needed varied activities to occupy the long evening hours after he returned from school.

Pete always liked food and had a favourite Indian restaurant. Initially, he was puzzled by Indian meals and reluctant to eat them. He didn't think that rice should be yellow and chicken red. When we had a takeaway, I would cook him something else. Then on one occasion, he put his spoon into the serving dish. We gave him a small helping and he wanted more. He overcame his reluctance and the first time we took him to the restaurant, it was clear he felt at home. He settled on the velvet bench. When it was time to leave, he cried. The waiters stood round astounded. On his seventeenth birthday, we invited his friend, Wendy, to join us there for a meal. Pete sat alongside her, smiling, enjoying the occasion.

After we retired, we continued to be busy. I still felt compelled to work on issues relating to the lives of people with learning disabilities and their families. I became a consultant, taking on projects, a trustee for three years of a small charity, Voice UK, which supported people with learning disabilities who had experienced crime or abuse, which sadly still happens too often. I was later a trustee of the National Family Carer Network, linking organisations and individuals supporting families of adults with learning disabilities, knowing how important it is to communicate their specific needs. Sadly neither of these small charities exists today.

There were also trips and visits to friends and places in the area which always prompted memories of Peter.

The sugar-beet factory on the edge of the town was a striking landmark with its cylindrical towers and tall chimneys. Now we are always pleased to see it on our trips from Dorset because on alternate Fridays Pete would go to the Gateway Club in a large room in its social club. Wendy and her friends would be waiting for him. He would make himself at home. Often when we returned to fetch him, he would be sitting in the middle of the disco, enjoying the music and the movements of others. But occasionally, for no apparent reason, nothing would persuade him to go into the club and he would push his way back to the car.

If we drove south of the town, we could reminisce that Wendy's home was nearby. For two years, after she moved to a different school, she would come and have tea with Pete once a week. He was pleased to see her and would grin. She would play her recorder to him, and he would smile broadly. Then he and I would drive the eight miles to her village to take her home.

We also began to introduce Pete to the local Causeway group, an ecumenical house group for adults with learning disabilities. He attended a carol service and party and went to a couple of evening meetings at my friend Nadia's home in a nearby village. He, Martin and Russell were by far the youngest. I recall him sitting in a circle, leaning across and slapping Russell's hand and them both smiling conspiratorially.

Driving through the countryside reminded us that summer evenings were easier with Peter as we could drive out to open spaces. Sometimes I had a picnic tea prepared for his return from school and we would drive to a picnic site in the country parks nearby. I remember an old friend coming up from London for the day. I thought the easiest way to entertain her and keep Peter happy was to drive up through the forest to a clearing where there were some picnic tables among the trees. It was she, the city dweller, who felt uneasy being in a remote place with no others in sight

On other occasions we would go out later in the evening to a village pub garden. On my last birthday before Pete's illness, we decided to go for a pub meal. Pete was not very hungry as he had expected tea on his return from school and we could not make him understand that it would be better to wait. Sitting with us in the lounge bar, he happily lingered over the food. Eventually we decided it was time to leave. Pete picked up his plate to take the remains of his meal home and we were just able to rescue it and leave it on the bar before we went out of the door.

On Sunday mornings, we always went to church in Ingham, the next village to Culford. Pete sat at a table with his catalogues, patting them and turning the pages. We would dread him deciding that there were more interesting ones in the lobby and diving off to find them in the middle of the readings. Sometimes he would head for the door during the sermon. Usually he settled. When it was a communion service, in the Peace everyone would come up to Pete to shake his hand. He was happy. At communion, he always would kneel beside us. He would look up questioningly: I am sure he wondered why he received a blessing and not the bread and wine. We always tried to steer him firmly past the organ, in case he decided to sit by Viv or Phil, as he did on one occasion. He could never be close enough to music. Sometimes he would stay in the church at the end of the service and have a drink and biscuit. At other times he would go back to the car and listen to Radio One while we had a coffee.

At one stage there was an American family in the congregation. Martha the mother, whose sister had Down's syndrome, taught her little Nicholas to say, 'Hi, Pete'. Sometimes in the middle of the prayers a voice would call, 'Hi, Pete'. Nicholas often wandered around the church during the service. One day Pete took Martha's hand and tried to get her to pick Nicholas up. Although he was not a model of good behaviour himself, he had high standards for others.

Sadly after Peter died, we felt too raw to continue to worship at Ingham and went instead to Great Livermere, another church within the benefice where the only memory of Pete was of him being unsettled and trying to leave. For the Millenium a local woodcarver was commissioned to make a crib scene for the group of churches. We funded the Mother and Child in memory of Pete, a reminder of his membership of that small welcoming congregation in Ingham.

We of course travelled further afield. While we were still living in East Anglia, I took a friend to visit Ely. It was several years since we had been with Peter. The town had gone up-market in the interim, no longer a café by the river but a restaurant. I recalled how on one occasion we had parked the car and were walking with Peter along the towpath. We decided we would have tea at a table looking out at the river. The service was slow. Pete gave me a shove as much as to say, 'Go in the kitchen and sort things out'.

Gradually he realised that being in a café or restaurant could mean waiting. However, despite there being an opportunity for a snack, he was ambivalent about Ely. The best days he would walk along the towpath holding Andy's arm, interested in craft on the river; on the worst days he wouldn't get out of the car. We couldn't always understand his reactions.

One of our most frequent excursions was to Felixstowe. I guess from Pete's perspective walking along the promenade was comparatively easy. There was plenty to see, the sea and other people; there were benches if he needed a rest; there was the prospect of a visit to the cafe at the Pavilion. On a mild February day, I recall Pete going onto the shingle, sitting down and removing his jumper and shirt. People looked at us very critically as he sat on the beach, bare-chested. He never seemed to feel the cold and was always keen to remove his anorak. Indeed, he took off his coat at the Huntingdon races one Boxing Day. We had arranged the rug between cars parked in the field and laid out the picnic, books and musical toys. Pete settled down to enjoy himself while Andy and Philip rushed off to the barrier to see the action. I am not even sure Pete knew there were horses to watch. We kept feeling his hands, his neck to make sure he wasn't freezing.

I think our favourite outings were always to the sea. Memories come flooding back: Sunday lunch in a pub restaurant in Aldeburgh, picnics on the sand at Southwold, walking the length of the promenade at Frinton to find the toilets, discreetly hidden from sight, a trip to Cromer to look at my grandparents' house where I stayed as a child, wandering along the water's edge at Wells-next -the -Sea. On a memorable, but very hot day at Wells we took the miniature railway that runs to the coast alongside the mile-long sea wall. We walked back, exhilarated by the sight of the boats and sounds of the gulls and Pete, with our encouragement, walked steadily along. As we finally reached the town, he sat down exhausted on the low wall. He was even too tired to cross the road to the fish-and-chip shop. Andy had to go and buy a takeaway for us all.

Particularly poignant are my memories of our last trip to Wells with Pete. It was a mild Sunday in early December. We decided to miss the Christingle service, as the previous year he had been restless. The Church had been full with chairs crammed into extra rows. I think he found it unfamiliar and overcrowded. We arrived at the coast in the late morning and walked along the front. We went this time into the fish-and-chip shop and sat by the window, looking across the road to the moored boat and beyond to the salt marshes, slowly eating our meal. We then continued our walk. From the pub on the corner came the sound of music. We looked in and saw four jazz musicians playing. We sat at a table close to them for an hour. Pete was absorbed, a wide grin spread across his face. We wanted to return home in the light. The musicians called 'goodbye' as we left.

For a long time the East Anglian seascape seemed bleak and lonely. It was a while before we wished to return to it. Now we love the salt marshes and wide skies, the flint houses and church towers on the horizon and reminders of happy times with Pete. On one of our most recent holidays near the coast in Suffolk, on our return journey to Dorset we drove past the entrance to Stonham Barns, one of Pete's favourite places, with its familiar wide entrance and notice boards alongside. In the café the staff came to know Pete and would prepare his fruit juice and ice cream without being asked. I can remember the day that Andy had to do a rugby tackle to stop Pete taking himself into the kitchen to find more. It reminded us of the many miles we would cover in an afternoon as it was twenty-eight miles from the bungalow! On Sunday afternoons, we so often drove round the country lanes crossing the gentle Suffolk landscape, listening to country and western or to Simon and Garfunkel tapes. Pete usually appreciated stopping somewhere where we could buy a snack.

CHAPTER SIX

'We weren't sure where the transition class would lead.'

WE SOMETIMES WENT with Pete over the border into Essex. We had become friends with Pete's teacher, Judy, who helped him so much soon after our arrival in Suffok, when he went to the local special school. We continued to visit her and her husband when they moved away, both in Pete's lifetime and after. In a condolence letter she wrote of 'the joy of knowing Pete'. I remember how, when he arrived at their house, Pete would make himself at home in the lounge. He used to like to sit on the floor and to pile up several gluten free biscuits on the coffee table as he was looking at his catalogues. He had to learn that that wasn't a good idea when Judy's spaniel, Corky, was around.

When thinking about the school, I can also see his classroom assistant, Mac, who worked with Judy. Mac later visited Pete in hospital, bringing a little book about cats that we would read to him again and again. She was Pete's mainstay.

'He was always such a good boy.'

He always was for her, although he eventually towered over her.

'Come along, Pete, and help me make the coffee.'

He would follow her out of the room.

A special class was made soon after Pete went to the school, following our move from Durham. It was for those who needed more help than could be provided in a main class with other students of their age. It was called Transition. Nicki, Neil and

Claire were the other students Pete knew well. Judy inspired them through her enthusiasm, creatively using texture and colour and giving them new experiences. There was particular excitement when Corky occasionally came into the classroom. He was gentle and loved by the children. Pete appreciated it when he barked. He thought that was what dogs should do!

In his class Pete particularly liked Claire, a tall girl with dark hair who, like him, didn't use words. One day on an outing to the Abbey gardens, when Pete was about eight, he took Claire's hand as they were pushed along in their major buggies, side by side. This was a big step for Pete as he was not very tactile. The psychiatrist took it as evidence that Pete was not autistic. He was clearly sociable, although his love of repetition, dislike of the unexpected and inability to play imaginatively can be characteristic of some children on the spectrum.

On several birthdays, Claire came to our bungalow with her parents for celebrations. One summer's day we went to her house for a barbecue. In the afternoon, her parents had arranged a visit to their cousin's deer farm for a treat. As we walked across the grass and among the trees Pete kept sitting down. He was not very impressed with the rural scene.

We weren't sure where the transition class would lead. When it was originally formed, the name implied that there would be movement. After several years with first Judy and then Richard as their teachers, the little group was attached to Greta's class and eventually they were integrated fully into the main class, always with Mac as Pete's assistant. Greta taught Pete country dancing. I remember, on one visit to the school, looking through the glass door to the hall and being pleased to see Pete ducking and weaving in a set. Another day I drove down a street in the town about a mile from the school. He was walking along in a small crocodile. I was most impressed.

As the school was tucked away in a cul-de-sac, it was not the building that subsequently prompted memories but individuals.

I caught sight of Claire at the college where I taught. One day, she was standing in the college garden. She was solemnly looking at Russell, who was talking loudly to his tutor. I walked by, a silent observer. Occasionally, in later years I saw Nicki and Neil walking round Bury with their support worker. No one would have realised the memories of Pete's friendships that these scenes evoked. I wonder what has happened to them later in their adult lives?

Where should Pete go to school at sixteen? For most students it was the local college but at that time, students like Pete who were non-verbal were unlikely to be accepted there at that age. I visited the college. I visited the Further Education Unit at Belstead School in Ipswich, where I was convinced that he would receive the individual help he needed, a decision I would never regret. When Pete was nearly fifteen, I went along to Belstead school again.

'Is there any chance Peter could come early and spend some time in the lower school?'

The head teacher was outstanding and I reckon she could move mountains, for within three weeks the decision was reached that Pete could start in the January, as he was fifteen. I shall never forget our early encounters with the school. Pete and I went on an initial visit and were given a tour of inspection. Everything was fine until we reached the swimming pool and Pete wanted to go in the water. Three adults had to be involved in moving him on!

The head asked me to come with Pete on the first day of term so that I could acquaint staff with his ways. She was not impressed with his propensity to sit down on the floor when he was confused or wanted his own way. I felt awful and that I had failed him. Could I have sought more help to manage Pete's behaviour? Should I have been firmer? It was always hard to unlearn bad habits! My mother picked me up over the phone that night.

'You have always done everything you can for Pete. No one can take that from you.'

Erica was Pete's teaching assistant in the first term at Belstead. Her memories of that first day are more comfortable than mine. In the afternoon, the class took the minibus to Lavenham and they visited the church. Pete made himself at home sitting down in a pew. When it was time to leave and Pete was walking down the path Erica asked him if he was sorry to leave. He sat down on the path.

She recalled, 'Dear Pete, you told us how you felt in the only way you could.'

He seemed to put his past behind him. Soon after his change of school, we invited Claire and her parents over to our bungalow not wanting to separate him from his friend. He sat close to the music video and Claire came and sat near him. We felt sad that on this occasion he took little notice of the girl who had been his companion for seven years. He had in the past always appeared to be reassured when she was present.

CHAPTER SEVEN

'His smile and deep chortle will always remain with me.'

I LIKE TO think about how much Pete enjoyed his life at Belstead, his two terms in the lower school and seven in the further education unit. In an ideal world I would have preferred him to have been educated throughout his schooling in a mainstream setting, as long as there was specialist and sufficient support, but that was not available. This would be more likely now, particularly for primary age children with special needs, but there is still a long way to go before children are all educated together. Belstead school made many links into the community and with a nearby mainstream school and had high expectations for its students. Sadly, it no longer exists.

After Pete's death his friends and teachers recorded their memories of his time there. We also have photos and diaries. I can picture his days. The timetable was individual: for Peter it was a new experience to move around a larger school building to different teachers and different lessons. He had a base however and at the beginning and end of each day he spent time with his tutor group. His tutor in the lower school reminded me that his first friends were Terry, Gary, Dawn, Robin, Carl and Tim. They remembered how at the end of the afternoon, Pete liked to eat his crisps, while they chatted about the day and prepared to go home.

There was a whole range of subjects to be followed: swimming, woodwork, art, religious education, communication, physical education, life skills. The range was extensive. He regularly went riding once a way was found for him to accept a helmet: his teacher perched on the gate and placed it on his head as he went past on Jessie, a suitably sturdy horse. In the lower school, he was bound by the National Curriculum. I love a photo of him and a fellow student, Luke, blowing bubbles in one of the science sessions.

In some lessons he could revel in physical sensations and sounds. Trampolining was one of his favourite activities. According to his teacher, 'He always eagerly climbed the steps into the middle of the bed and with a huge grin on his face held hands and bounced... I will always remember him doing seat-drops, a skill that requires energy, coordination and a lot of daring.'

Another teacher wrote, 'He gained much enjoyment from the sensory room, especially the plasma ball, bubble tubes and torches... his smile and deep chortle will always remain with me.' For another there were memories of the one-to-one sessions in the soft playroom.

'Pete always went to the top of the "hill" where he sat cross legged, and I would sit cross legged next to him. We always had music on and would play games, clapping hands together, along with the music. I would imitate any little gestures and movements Pete made and he would giggle.'

Another popular lesson was computing. He would use a touch screen. He especially liked the programme, *Haunted House*. He loved the ghost appearing from behind the door and would touch the same point on the screen repeatedly.

Music of course gave him enormous pleasure. The head of the lower school wrote, 'He had his favourites: brass bands, calypso music, pop music, in fact any lively music that was loud enough for him to hear and to enjoy. I can see his face before me now, smiling broadly as he rocked to the rhythm of our singing and playing. I would always sit on Pete's left side, his good ear and sometimes Pete would lift my guitar to his ear and really revel in the vibrations.'

Not unsurprisingly food inspired him. The domestic science teacher recalled,

'We spent many happy hours together cooking various dishes but cakes were always his favourite. I have many happy memories, which I shall always treasure, especially Pete's happy personality and wonderful sense of humour and the way he loved to put his cakes in and out of the box. He never wanted to eat them- just to admire them.'

He would carry them round the school for the rest of the day and bring them home very proudly. If he had made a loaf of gluten-free bread, he would always make short work of it. I personally felt slightly guilty that amid our busy lives, I didn't bake but collected the bread on prescription from the chemist. It was easier but looked much less appetizing!

The lunch hours were a challenge. His midday supervisor wrote to me,

'I was given charge of Peter on a one-to-one. Every day for six months, I spent one-and-a-half hours with him, supervising his lunch, toilets etc... I had tried for months to get Pete to trust me and to accept that I was with him at lunchtime. This particular day, Peter not only came over to me, grabbed my hand and took me to the kitchen hatch, but he also put his hands round my neck for a cuddle. From that day we were best friends.'

Moving to the further education unit brought greater freedom. At lunchtime there was a tuck shop and the students would play music. His friends recollected that Pete liked to watch Tracy dance. The head of the unit noted, 'Pete was selective about his friends, but nobody quite measured up to Tracy. Tracy was a bit of a dare devil and he liked that. She was also an exciting dancer. Although not much of a dancer himself, he used to follow Tracy while she was dancing at break and lunch times.'

I reflect sadly that because Tracy was in the care of the local authority when she was eighteen, she was moved to another area, away from her friends and all that was familiar. Why have we been so slow to recognise the importance of friendship? Why do authorities sever relationships? The Friendship Club is the bedrock of People First Dorset, where I am now a trustee. As William tells us and is quoted on the website: 'I only used to have one friend, very little confidence and had hate crime. The Friendship Club at People First Dorset changed all that. Thanks to this club I now have lots of friends who I see at events and some I've learnt to meet independently.' [3]

How did Peter feel losing contact with his special friend?

These memories we were given of Pete at school are very positive. We know there were difficult moments too, but the whole approach of the school was to emphasise a pupil's strengths and to meet individual needs and these extended to preparing them for their life after school.

3 People First Dorset https:// www.peoplefirstdorset.org.uk

CHAPTER EIGHT

'George said he thought Pete was happy.'

AS HE BECAME older, Peter would spend time each week in the training flat at his school, so that he could become more independent. He would go out to buy his ingredients for cooking. His tutor recalled, 'We would shop together at Tesco and Pete would sit down when he came to the jam. He would choose the flavour he wanted. Once back in school he would sit and concentrate for so long while we cooked the meal together.'

I guess he identified the labels in the same way as he would choose crisps by the colour of the packet at home.

Sue, the head of the further education unit, recalled his enjoyment of discos. 'He sat on the floor, his shoes and socks off, rocking to and fro laughing his head off to the music. He loved every minute of it. Every so often he would stop and simply look around absorbing the atmosphere and smiling to himself. Such a lovely memory.'

Sometimes special outings were planned. One summer Pete went sailing and appeared so at ease that the staff asked if he had been previously with us. He had in fact been restricted to a pedalo on a boating lake by the sea and a trip in a substantial launch on the Helston River where the owner allowed Philip to be at the steering wheel for the return trip!

Twice Pete went to London to see musicals. *Buddy* was, I think, his favourite. He sat close to the front, away from the main school party so that he could see and hear. He happened to be next to an American who was on holiday in the UK. Pete's assistant recalled that he was a little restless before the performance began and became agitated when the lights went down. However, she would never forget the pleasure on his face as he recognised the music coming from the stage. He babbled and rocked and hummed. He was so very, very happy. At the end of the performance, the American said he had never experienced such a wonderful afternoon and Pete had given him such joy that he would never forget.

At Pete's funeral, Richard, his vicar from Ingham, asked the congregation to picture an occasion from his life. Later his head teacher and Suzanne, a classroom assistant, told me they exchanged brief smiles, aware that they were thinking of the same episode. They had taken a group of students in the minibus deep into the Suffolk countryside for a walk. After fifty yards, Pete sat down. They realised from his expression that this was not just a reluctance to walk or a protest because there was no café, but because he needed a toilet. Pete always sat down on the toilet and would never agree to stand and so disappearing behind some bushes was not an option. Fortunately, a man was working nearby and they asked if there was a toilet anywhere. He pointed to a hut at some distance. Pete seemed to understand and leaving the rest of the group with another teacher, Pete, the head and Suzanne set out across the field. When they drew close to their destination, they found the man clearing the way with his scythe and apologising that there were going to be spiders inside. Nobody minded. They were pleased to find a solution to Pete's problem. The class then had their walk.

Sometimes we went to events organised by the Friends of the school. When we went to the Christmas fair, Pete turned round and rushed out of the building, upset that the school was overrun by stalls and crowds. He was happier at a social afternoon at a sports club and, on another occasion, watching the head teacher and others abseil down a silo at the sugar beet factory to raise funds.

It was apparent after Pete's death how much many of his contemporaries liked him. Their memories were recorded for us. They showed an appreciation of his ways, his liking for crisps, the removal of his boots and glasses. The remark that meant the most to us was the one made by George: he said that he thought Pete was happy. A few months after Pete's death, we went to the school to talk about spending the money that our friends had donated in his memory. A lift had been installed and this meant that there was a new wall at the end of the library. We took over a catalogue so that we could choose two pictures to hang there. We sat round a table with Pete's friends. Sue, the head of the unit explained what we were doing. 'That wall is so bare.'

His friend, Maria giggled. We all looked at a book with some of Van Gogh's pictures. Should it be the sunflowers, the chair, the bedroom, the bridge, the café at night? Pete had liked examining these with Andy when he was in the Chantry. We were beginning to think it might be the bridge, then we turned back a couple of pages and found a picture of the promenade at Olonne.

'With the beach huts, it's a bit like Felixstowe. Pete liked going there.'

His friends, George and Daniel looked pleased. I hadn't realised that they lived there. Everyone liked the idea of the seaside.

'Perhaps we could have the café for the second picture. Pete always loved going to a café.'

The others agreed with my suggestion.

Sue took us down to the courtyard. The school was going to order some wooden garden furniture. Pete always appreciated a bench. We all reminisced about walking along the front at Felixstowe and how sometimes he stopped at every seat. We agreed that if there was any money over, it would be spent on a picnic basket. Sue told us how, on outings, Pete expected to have a place especially laid, while his friends were happy to have a sandwich in their hand. He clearly liked order, although I don't think it was his upbringing. We in the family were perfectly happy to do without plates and knives and forks on a picnic. Every time I see wooden picnic tables I am reminded of Pete. We had to avoid them unless we had some food with us. On one occasion he tried to join another family and we had to firmly guide him away. We returned to the school a second time to hang the pictures and to inspect the benches. During one visit, his friend Dawn sat beside me and said simply, 'I miss Pete.'

CHAPTER NINE

'We have all these memories of Scotland thanks to Philip.'

APART FROM OUR visits to our home in North Yorkshire, the furthest Pete travelled was to Cornwall and Scotland. When he was eight, we rented a wooden chalet on a campsite on the Roseland peninsula. He was not impressed by this dark small building and began to howl as soon as we arrived. We feared we might have to make the eight-hour journey back to Suffolk. Then as he calmed down a little, we showed him the narrow room he was to share with Philip, a bed against each wall and his tape recorder. He began to settle, and we enjoyed our week.

Some years later when he was in his teens, we rented a wooden chalet on a site amid pine trees in Galloway. The journey was long. We took the minor winding roads across the Pennines and then the major road along the Solway Firth. This time he made himself more at home: his first action on arrival was to strip off his clothes and climb into the bath. I don't know why he did this. The sight of the bath may have prompted his decision or he may have had a tummy ache, as he often wanted to get into water if he had one. We boiled up some kettles as the immersion heater wasn't on. Once Pete realised he had his music tapes with him and that he was again sharing a room with Philip, he was happy.

Most days we would set out to explore the coast and have picnics on the beaches. One morning, Andy wanted to play golf and Philip took on his father's role, helping entertain Pete by the sea. One day we headed inland to the forests and lochs. We drove long distances but spent some time climbing up a rocky path to overlook the water. On the last evening we decided to go out for a meal in a local pub, early in the evening before it became crowded. Once we were settled at the table, Pete removed his boots. He was showing he felt comfortable. I used to get anxious that he would do this when adult, when it would be less acceptable - a needless worry on my part.

The most memorable event of the week was Pete learning to swim unaided. Most days we would go into the little pool on the site. Despite my loud protests, Philip decided to remove Pete's arm bands, first one and then the other. Pete continued to do his distinctive dog paddle with no problem.

'Pete can swim.'

'Well done, Pete!'

I am sure our cries were heard all over the park.

We have all these memories of Scotland thanks to Philip for he was insistent that Pete should come on holiday with us that year. Sometimes we would take Philip on holiday and Pete would go away to a centre for respite care. We were fortunate that, as we were both teaching, we had holidays where we could give time to both boys but nonetheless, we wanted sometimes to be able to give all our attention to Philip. We had previously taken him to Wales, Majorca and Crete. That year we had asked Philip where he would like to go, expecting him to suggest somewhere in Europe.

'I want Pete to come on holiday with us.'

We have Philip to thank for those good memories.

Sometimes people speak as if it is a disadvantage to have a disabled brother or sister. I know several for whom it has been such a positive influence on their lives. I think of Rachel, David's sister who went into the health service and Zoe who works at People First Dorset.

I was encouraged recently to read Philip's take on his experience: 'I grew up with a brother who had profound learning disabilities. He taught me how to value the experiences and wisdom that were not considered "normal", this has given me a passion for social justice and people having control over their own lives and also the importance of community working together for change.'[4]

As I think back to Pete's other expeditions outside Suffolk during his teenage years, Andy's school trip to Alton Towers each autumn was a highlight and Pete went three times. Shows, rides, picnic areas, a long bus journey, there were all the ingredients of a good day out, especially as the weather was always fine. Pete was disappointed that we were not keen on accompanying him on the more exhilarating rides. One day at another theme park Pete made a beeline for the pirate ship and was on it before we could stop him. Andy had to jump on too and it was he who looked slightly green after that experience!

Occasionally we had trips to Sussex to see Andy's parents. One particularly memorable day was their Golden Wedding celebration, a Sunday in July 1990. We all drove down to Andy's brother's house for a buffet lunch. Dick, Eileen, Pete's cousin John, and their little dog Chloe were there to greet us as we unloaded our contributions. I remember Pete sitting on the floor by a coffee table, enjoying the meal, smiling at his grandparents, Andy's mother finding the occasion overwhelming with all her immediate family around her. Then the scene shifts to the garden. It was one of those scorching summer days. We had brought Pete's pool with us and he needed to sit in it to remain cool. Some of us took chairs outside. Andy's parents departed later in the afternoon and we began to gather up our belongings for the long drive home. As we were standing by the front door, saying our goodbyes, Pete pushed Chloe with his foot to make her bark. In his view that was what was fascinating about dogs. He knew Corky had a good bark! 'Pete how could you? You're a naughty boy!' He did have the grace to look contrite.

4 Morgan, P., Rose, S and Dyer, R. (2019) Co- Production: The essential component in recovery colleges in Burhouse, A and Denney, J (eds.) in *Implementing Recovery College: One Trust's Journey* Available from https://www.swrecoverycollege.nhs.uk/wp-content/uploads/How-to-Manual_newdraft_V11_editable-version_4.pdf-

On the Culford School half marathon with his dad

At the swimming pool

Paddling with Jill at Scarborough

Enjoying looking at a catalogue

In Dalby Forest with Philip

On the trampoline

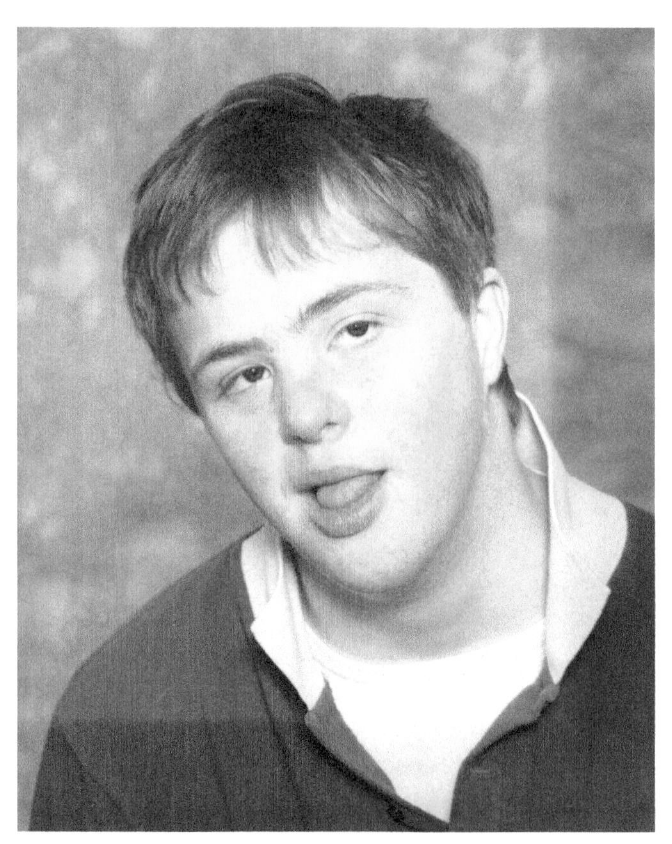

School photo

Playing Haunted House

Cooking at school

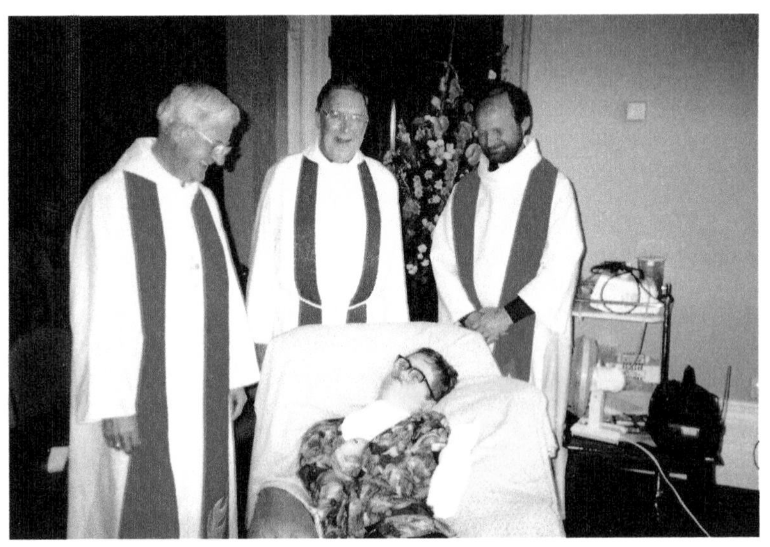

At his confirmation with Bishop Jonathan Bailey, Canon Richard Norburn and Revd Peter Gibbs

CHAPTER TEN

'Pete really enjoyed being in the middle of a vigorous game of cricket, even if he spent most of the time sitting down.'

OUR MOST FREQUENT destination outside Suffolk was North Yorkshire, to our own home. This enabled us to have lots of holidays on the Yorkshire coast in a place that was familiar, which was always helpful for Pete as we knew he did not like new places. Recently we went north to hold a memorial service for my aunt who had died after over three years in a care home near us in Dorset. We wanted to celebrate her life with family and friends in the village outside Whitby where she had lived for forty years. It was a week we also remembered my parents who had retired to the Moors and of course Pete. One grey August evening eighteen of the family gathered on the beach at Sandsend for fish and chips and drinks, especially to remember them all.

During our week away, Andy and I drove up the road that went along the back of the garden of the bungalow near Whitby, our first home, remembering our times there. We didn't go to Scarborough to see the house we subsequently bought. We could picture it. We purposely had chosen one with a downstairs bedroom so that Pete would be safe. What did he do when he first arrived at the house but go immediately upstairs. Nevertheless, I believe he liked his room on the front on the corner on the ground floor. At night instead of looking out on darkness, there were streetlights and car headlamps. He would get out of bed and look out of the window, often tugging down the curtains in his excitement. He seemed to like the spaciousness of the house and the patio where we had barbecues.

We would go and visit my parents, then living in a flat overlooking the North Bay. In the July, almost a year after we bought the Scarborough house, my father was very ill. Pete would have been eleven and was suffering from measles. As soon as he was well enough, I rushed north, leaving Pete with Andy and Philip. They had to tell him about his grandfather's death.

The first time Pete went to the flat after that, he went and looked closely at the large brown arm chair his grandfather had always sat in and picked up his photo from the table alongside it, something he had never done before. I am sure he understood that his grandfather had died. Because he could not talk, we sometimes risked underestimating what he could take in. We always talked to him about everything that was going on. There were of course times when he could not comprehend something and then he might become agitated.

My mother liked to invite us to tea in her flat and to the bungalow she purchased later. Pete would lie across the floor, his ear on his cassette recorder keeping one eye on proceedings. He would suddenly get up to find the yellow pages in the hall cupboard for it would provide him with satisfying images and pages to turn and pat or he would go and check whether the tea was laid. Sometimes my mother would join us on the beach. We would place ourselves strategically close to the toilets. This meant passing a promenade café. Pete loved going there and often we had to steer him firmly past the outside tables.

'I think of Pete whenever I walk by the café,' my mother used to tell me.

Pete had an uncanny sense of where places were. On one occasion he became agitated when we deviated from a usual route. I wonder if he had a mind map of cafés he liked.

Often, we would drive out of Scarborough. Our favourite place was always Whitby. Sometimes we would linger on the

West Cliff. We might play crazy golf, with Pete watching or joining in as he pleased, or we could ride on the little train or Pete might go on the large trampolines and, with our encouragement, show off the skills that he had learnt at school. We might walk down the zigzag path or linger in the café in the Spa Pavilion, looking out at the North Sea, sometimes taking the lift on to the beach and more often back up. We might approach the beach by walking down the Khyber Pass to the harbour arm. We could stop and play in the amusement arcades. Pete enjoyed the razzmatazz and particularly liked sitting in the booth watching the car races, turning the steering wheel. Once on the sand we might have a picnic or buy fish and chips. Pete might sit on a rug looking at his catalogues. He loved wandering by the sea. We did not know why he always headed to his left, paddling on the edge of the shallow water. As he got older, some parents guided their small children away from him. What did they fear? He would not hurt them.

Sometimes in the summer holidays, Roger my brother, his wife and two sons, Tom and Ben, would come and stay with our parents and then later my mother. We would meet up on the sand. Philp and his two cousins' mission in life was to dig the most enormous hole that they could. Vigorously they would pile up the sand. Pete slightly bemused by this activity would sit on his rug keeping a weather eye on proceedings. On our recent family trip, Philip, Tom and Ben, decades on, reminisced about their exploits as boys and recalled with amusement how they dug for 'colloil', the elusive treasure they hoped to find.

I can also picture Andy's brother, Dick, his wife, Eileen, and their son, John, on the beach with us. They came up from the south for a couple of holidays. Pete seemed to be particularly attached to his uncle and we have photos of him when he was little, sitting on Dick's knee clapping hands. Although the brothers were not strikingly physically alike, they had very similar voices. Was that reassuring to Pete?

On a Sundays there could be the treat of a brass band playing. We could sit on one of the benches by the bandstand close to the harbour and be sure that Pete was going to enjoy the next hour, although he could be restless between items. Late one Sunday afternoon, after listening to the music, we were making our way along the quayside. At the end of a group of buildings was a café. Very quickly Pete dived in. Should we say 'No Pete, not today' or should we agree it was a good time for a meal? We decided on the latter and Pete was very pleased with himself, as we settled at a table by the wall, ordered food and then ate a leisurely tea together. I also recall one Boxing Day when we drove to Whitby and the last café before the harbour was open. We went inside and ordered a snack for Pete and coffees for ourselves. Several other tables were occupied, and it became almost a small party as people began to talk to one another. Cafés were often places where we could all relax.

We also enjoyed going to Sandsend, a much quieter place than Whitby, and spending time on the beach and perhaps in the pub garden. One day Pete made it clear that he didn't think spending time on a nearly deserted beach was much fun. Even starting the picnic failed to reconcile him and he grabbed his box and headed off to the car. We had to return to Whitby, but even then, he wasn't prepared to set out to walk down the Khyber Pass, presumably thinking that he would have to climb back again. That was one of those days when everyone returned home feeling frustrated.

When we were planning where to go, Filey was often a close runner-up to Whitby. We would go to the car park at the southern end of the town, close to the sea and a park. Again Pete particularly liked heading off across the grass to the outdoor café and we would often have to steer him away. One day we took him on a pedalo on the small boating lake. He enjoyed the movement and seeing us negotiate other boats, a smile across his face. We walked down the lane to the sea, which ensured

Pete had a reasonable amount of exercise. Where we settled was determined by the state of the tide.

One Sunday some friends with three of their children joined us on the beach in Filey and Pete really enjoyed being in the middle of a vigorous game of cricket, even if he spent most of the time sitting down. It was one of those days that he didn't wish to end. He then lured us into the beachside café and grinned with pleasure as we sat down and delayed the walk up to the car park.

Pete seemed to have mixed feelings about Bridlington. There we would park to the north and take the path to the promenade and try to walk some distance before going on the beach. One day we must have walked for about a mile and felt that we had done well in persuading Pete to go so far. On the next occasion, he must have remembered this; he sat down on the ground as we came out of the car park and was very reluctant to walk anywhere. We did have the alternative of taking the 'land train' that ran down the promenade.

Somehow trips inland never had the same quality as those hours we lingered near or by the sea. If we decided to go inland, Dalby Forest was our most likely destination. There were the necessary ingredients: toilets, picnic tables and a short walk, this time alongside a small lake. Once a year we'd try to go to Flamingo Land and Pete would enjoy the zoo, the funfair and the circus. We managed a trip to the Jorvik museum in York, by arranging that we didn't have to queue. On one of my mother's birthdays, we tried to combine a day that would satisfy Pete and give her a treat. We drove to a country house where there were impressionist paintings on the top floor. Pete and Andy stayed in the grounds while my mother and I looked at paintings by Renoir, Matisse, Corot and others. Looking back, I suspect she would have been happier with a day that Pete would have enjoyed more. She always made meeting his needs a priority.

Whatever the time of year, we enjoyed our visits to North Yorkshire with its dramatic coastline, places to visit and the opportunities to see relatives, my parents, my aunt and our brothers and their families. Sometimes friends would stay nearby and we would share outings. Recently, all these years later when some old friends visited, they brought photos they had taken on their holidays near us all those years ago. They told us that they had made a photo book of their daughter's life for her fortieth birthday and included pictures of her as a young girl with Pete. They emailed us copies of the photos. On one, she looks at him as he stands taking in what the other children are doing, on another he joins them clambering on a log frame. We didn't know he had made such an impression on her.

North Yorkshire offered us an escape from the pressures of term time. We had many alternative activities: the sea, the beach, seaside amusements, car rides across the open moorland or near the rugged coast. There were plenty of opportunities for picnics and meals in cafés. We could meet with family and friends. On a couple of occasions Philip invited a school friend to come and stay. There was something for everybody.

After Pete's death, it was seven years before I could return. It would have been empty and desolate. The memories were too painful. Andy would have found it a comfort to have returned sooner. Now I am pleased to go north and recall those holidays. I am glad that this summer we could hold the Thanksgiving service for my aunt's life in the church she had attended near Whitby and could be reminded again of Pete's appreciation of being in the north.

CHAPTER ELEVEN

'If Margaret was busy in her office, he would go and sit on the floor by her open door. "Come on Pete, it is time for you to go back and see the others".'

AFTER OUR RECENT visit to North Yorkshire, we travelled on to Durham for a weekend, driving through Middlesbrough. The industrial landscape was familiar although we didn't drive past Eston House in Teesside where Pete had been used to going away for short breaks from an early age. It was run by two remarkable nuns. Pete's first head teacher recommended it to us, 'You need to have time to recharge your batteries and to spend time with your other son. I would trust my children to Sister Mac'. It was a scary thought to leave Pete with someone else but when we met Sister Mac we were reassured. She was warm, capable and welcoming but clearly had high expectations of the young Catholic volunteers she trained. Pete was able to continue visiting there after our move south. Sister Mac liked to provide continuity in care. Pete was supported first by Ann and then by Jill, who were with him at all times, sharing a room at night. I think their experience had a major impact on their lives. Ann became a learning disability nurse while Jill went into teaching.

When he was approaching puberty Pete was assigned a young man to look after him. This was a great success apart from one respect: the volunteers were expected to look after their charges' clothes, and until then he had arrived back home with his belongings clean and neatly packed. This time when we opened Peter's case a tumble of dirty and clean clothes fell out including a pair of a nun's knickers which I had to pack up and return by post. Eventually, Peter became too old to visit and that chapter in his life came to an end. Jill, who had looked after him the most often in earlier times came and spent several days with us one summer in Scarborough. We have photos of her paddling with Pete on the edge of the sea.

In Suffolk, Peter was assessed for eligibility for short breaks. We were very fortunate that there was the Family Help Unit, run by Scope, in the town. We can catch a glimpse of the roof as we drive along the A14 to stay with friends on our visits to East Anglia. It was a modern single storey building with large day rooms and a long corridor with bedrooms off. There was a wide-open space for outside play. Pete would go there occasionally for weekends and longer stays of up to a week in school holidays. Margaret, the manager was a particular favourite. She described how he would follow her around when she was on duty. If she was busy in her office, he would go and sit on the floor by her open door.

'Come on, Pete, it is time for you to go back and see the others.' After a while, she would take his hand and they would go back to the playroom together. Andy reminded me that Pete sometimes would want to sit in the stationary minibus. Was he imagining places he would like to travel? At one stage when my timetable at the college prevented me from being at home for Pete's school transport on one or two days, he would be dropped off there for tea and I would fetch him between five and half past.

The staff did everything they could to make his stay at the Unit enjoyable. As Pete was approaching school-leaving age, we knew that he would no longer be eligible and would have to go to adult provision. We didn't know how he would adapt to this change where he would be with much older adults. In the end we didn't find out. Once Peter was sixteen years old, he had a large increase in his state benefits and we decided we could use some of this money to provide him with some kind of continuity in his respite care. We decided to make some plans of our own. We found a charity, Break, in Norfolk, which at that time had two houses, one in Hunstanton and one in Sheringham, where he could go for a holiday both as a teenager and then later as an adult. There would be staff awake overnight. This gave us the assurance that if Pete started going there in his teenage years, he would be able to continue into adulthood.

Again we went through the stages needed to familiarise Peter with a new place and enabling them to get to know him a little too. Andy and I visited alone to discuss Pete's needs then we went with Pete, left him for a day, then overnight and then for a week. I shall never forget the first day he spent there. It was January. We were going to explore Kings Lynn for the six hours of his visit. There was a wind chill factor of -14 °C. We dashed from one historic site to another, taking refuge wherever we could and eventually lingering over a cup of tea in a hotel in front of a log fire, before fetching Pete.

Peter had two full week-long holidays at Break. There were daily outings in small groups. He is the only family member who spent time in the grounds of Sandringham. He was expected to take pocket money with him. As he did not appear to understand money, we had always bought things when we felt he needed them. Maybe we were wrong in this approach. We were pleased to receive a post card from him, and he came home with a present for us. A large white vase with a pink flower design he gave me is now on a windowsill, a constant reminder of that small part of Peter's life.

Suffolk Social Services also had a Link scheme whereby children with special needs were assessed to see if they were eligible for being linked with a family, a couple or an individual. Peter was seen as difficult to place and we helped to make a special poster with his photo, expressing his need. It felt strange to have him portrayed in this way. It paid off and we appreciated that Pete could go to visit Margaret and John as part of the scheme. They were ideal as they both worked supporting adults with learning disabilities in residential settings. He went to their home. He sometimes stayed overnight and had his own room, with his catalogues ready for him. He would make Margaret laugh as he expected to keep John company watching the television, while she prepared food. I do not know where Pete acquired such chauvinist views, as his father and brother would help in the kitchen.

I would hear how he would do things that were unheard of at home. On one occasion, he helped Margaret tidy out the kitchen cupboard and on another played hide-and-seek with her in the garden. Pete was made to feel special and was clearly at home. I can see him now, waving goodbye vigorously to encourage me to leave and to stop chatting with Margaret. On one occasion, Margaret had a friend staying and Pete apparently glowered at her all the time. He was however content to share the attention with her cats. Tinkerbell was his favourite. He was even known to slip her some food, which was a sure sign that he liked her. I feel very glad that John and Margaret visited Pete on the weekend before he died. These friendships were very valuable to him. As part of the Link scheme, we also had two possible people we could call upon in his later teenage years to sit in with him at home if Andy and I wanted to go out in the evening.

I have been reflecting how fortunate we were. I am sure that now families do not have the range of opportunities that we had. More recently from 2010 with the government policy of austerity, some services have disappeared and then during the pandemic others were withdrawn at least for a time. Families have been forced to rely more on their own resources. That has made life so hard while also depriving their sons and daughters of different experiences. It raises questions of what kind of a life people with learning disabilities should be able to expect and why we are allowing opportunities to be cut back.

CHAPTER TWELVE

'What kind of a future?'

IN THE MONTHS before Pete's illness, it is ironic now to think how anxious I was becoming about what would happen to him after he left school at the age of nineteen. Looking through papers I came across a note I had written, 'If we don't look at his future imaginatively, what kind of life will he have?'

I was asking whether Peter could continue with his education. He had made good progress at Belstead. Young people with learning disabilities were entitled to an education until the age of twenty-five. His brother had gone to university, why shouldn't Pete have a similar opportunity for learning? Where could he go? Would the local college take him on one of their courses? I knew it was unlikely he would meet their requirements. Would a residential college be too far from family and friends? Would we get funding? These questions teemed through my mind. I can reflect, sadly, that these are still the questions that gnaw away at parents and carers.

If there was no suitable college placement what would he do in the day time? Would going to a day centre enable him to progress? Would he have variety in his days? Was I like other parents, who talked of staring into an abyss when their sons and daughters were leaving full-time education which had provided a framework for their lives?

There was at that time a unit in the town for people described as having 'challenging behaviour'. Would the authorities think that was where Pete should go? What if that label was attached to him? I would resist that at all costs. His experience at Belstead School had shown that he flourished in an environment where there were people of different abilities and people responded to his strengths and interests.

Units working with people with challenging behavior now prompt unwelcome images. In recent years I have seen on our television screens two Panorama programmes revealing dreadful abuse, physical and verbal, at two NHS-funded assessment and treatment centres: Winterbourne View in 2011 and Whorlton Hall in 2019. However unlikely, I still imagine how it would have been for Peter and for us if he had ever found his way into such placements. Being often far from home and for long periods of time, how can this help? Shockingly there are still over two thousand people with learning disabilities in such units.

Thinking about what Pete would do in the daytime was important. Then when should he leave home to live more independently with support? I recall how some years before, when I was living in Durham doing an Open University course on disability, I had, as part of an assignment, interviewed an officer in the County Offices asking her about options for students leaving the special school. Then people were usually transported in minibuses to the adult training centre, next to Pete's first school, segregated from their community. Her picture in contrast was of someone living with support in their community, having help with shopping, cooking and other household tasks. That would be how they would spend their time in her view. I then felt that kind of a life was limiting. Now I reflect in many ways she was right – if there could be the additional ingredients of friendship, being part of a community, possibly some volunteering, some classes, a job. I see members of People First Dorset leading such a life. In our work at the Foundation for People with Learning Disabilities, we established through an inquiry and research projects, the importance to young people with learning disabilities of leading a full life and the adverse effects on their mental health if they were denied opportunities.[5 6]

We felt that in many ways it would be better for Pete to leave home to live more independently as a young man. Like other parents in a similar situation, we always had the nagging worry about what would happen to Pete as we aged, when we could no longer provide twenty-four-hour care. Would he not adjust to change better soon after leaving school than later on and appreciate the support of people closer to his age to lead a full life?

We decided to look at residential options close to our home and I made several visits, but either the waiting list was closed, or they were unsuitable, or I did not like the atmosphere. We did not want to unsettle Pete as it would take several years to implement any plans and so we decided only to take him somewhere that might be a possibility to gauge his reactions. The only place that Pete visited with us, was in North Essex: a group of bungalows, with workshops, a coffee shop for the local community and some outreach homes and businesses. We met the manager in the busy coffee shop and I can picture Pete sitting there enjoying the bustle and her talking to him. Even so, there were no vacancies.

Ruth came on the scene. She was the social worker who would implement the plan. She talked of a private home in Suffolk that was being set up. I was not sure about homes run for profit. I was planning to make an exploratory visit. It was decided that Pete would continue to live with us for a

---

5 Foundation for People with Learning Disabilities *Count Us In: The inquiry into meeting the mental health needs of young people with learning disabilities* (Foundation for People with Learning Disabilities 2002).

6 Foundation for People with Learning Disabilities *Making Us Count* (Foundation for People with Learning Disabilities 2005).

while after leaving school, finding day opportunities in the town, until plans for him to live more independently could be finalised. I meet parents who still have the same worries as we had about where their sons and daughters will live when they can no longer care, brows furrowed, anxiety written across their faces, tones serious as they contemplate the future. Later, when I was a consultant with the Foundation for People with Learning Disabilities, I evaluated a Mencap project, *Involve Me,* exploring ways of involving people with profound and multiple learning disabilities in decisions about their lives, a cause close to my heart. As part of the preparation, I had the privilege to meet Victoria Willson, who had the tenancy of a flat in Kings Cross for twenty-four years. She shared the flat with another young woman. She had twenty-four-hour support, was close to her family and lived the life of her choosing, until she sadly died in 2013. She was a role model for what is possible.[7]

We were fixed on finding a local setting where we could see Pete regularly and he could lead an interesting life. In the end, none of those questions had to be answered. The supreme irony was that when Pete went to live in the Sue Ryder Home, he was in mainstream provision for any younger person with a head injury and his learning disability was no longer a consideration.

7 See PCPLD Network https://www.pcpld.org/real-life-stories

CHAPTER THIRTEEN

'It is as if I am looking into another time, never to be regained.'

PICTURES OF PRAGUE flash across the television screen. As I look at Wenceslaus Square, the castle, the Baroque houses, the symmetry of the buildings, it is as if I am looking into another time, never to be regained, when everything seemed in its proper place.

During that holiday in 1994, Andy and I wandered round the streets, pursuing the history. Music was everywhere: buskers on Charles Bridge, classical concerts in the churches, folk groups in the squares. In the evenings we returned to the warm welcome of our Czech hosts. Despite the language barrier, we told them about Pete. We knew he was being well looked after in the Family Help Unit.

On our return after our twenty-four-hour coach journey, we spoke to Margaret, the manager whom Pete always thought of as his special friend. Pete had had a really good time until that day when he had gone down with a virus. Was that the beginning of his final illness? We shall never know. Certainly I felt Pete was never fully well again. His return to school for the autumn term was delayed. He had a course of antibiotics. For several weeks he was banging his head on the wall, on the window of the car. Gradually the symptoms appeared to recede.

Each year as I have looked back over the weeks preceding his strokes, the sad and the good memories intermingle. There was the Saturday evening, when Pete was invited, along with us, to his friend, Wendy's surprise eighteenth birthday party in a village hall some eight miles away. We arrived in good time. Wendy wasn't allowed to look as we came in the door.

'Oh Pete, it's lovely to see you,' she cried out as they removed hands from her eyes.

We sat at one of the tables at the side of the room, pulling party poppers and crackers. Pete enjoyed the food, specially prepared for him by Wendy's mum. Eventually we danced. Pete seemed unsteady on his legs.

'Anyone would think you'd been drinking,' we joked. How could we have been so lighthearted?

Pete had had a scan just after half term, when his legs had given way under him but that had not shown up any problems. He was referred to the consultant psychiatrist. He had a couple of mild seizures. We were thinking about medication and establishing contact with the community nurses. No one was aware how serious the situation was.

The outing to Wells ... the supper in the Charity Restaurant ... the Christmas Disco at his school where we marvelled at Pete's progress. Previously, if we were present, he had been reluctant to leave us, but now he sat in the middle of the floor among his friends, oblivious of our presence. We chatted with some other parents. I remember telling Karen's mum more about the plans for Pete's eighteenth birthday disco and supper to be held at Andy's school in January. We had sent out the invitations. Marion, one of his teachers, was going to borrow the school minibus and drive his friends across.

One of the final entries in Pete's school notebook was an account of the Christmas outing for a pub meal. Rather than have a party at school the students were able to decide what they would like to do. Pete's choice had been a great success. How did he indicate his preference? Was he shown pictures of venues to see how he reacted?

In that December, he had several severe seizures. I can remember one evening when Andy was out at school and I was sitting beside Pete on the settee. A glazed look came across his face and he was no longer 'with me'. As his awareness returned, he dragged himself out of the room and along the passage to our bedroom. I was half supporting him alarmed at his limited mobility. Gradually he seemed to recover, and Andy returned.

On the Wednesday two weeks before Christmas, Pete appeared really unwell, pale, vomiting, his movement impaired. We called out the duty GP, our own doctor being on holiday. He thought Pete might have a virus. Andy lay beside Pete the whole of the next night trying to prevent him from banging his head on the floor. The next day he was feverish and coughing. I rang the duty doctor for that day. Pete had pneumonia. He was prescribed antibiotics and I rushed into town. It was late-night Christmas shopping. Bands were playing carols. There was an air of jollity from which I felt totally removed.

Another disturbed night ... Pete's breathing became laboured ... we had to support him if he moved from his bed. Pictures of the Piéta came to my mind but I dismissed them.

At about 5.30 am we called the doctor again.

'I am afraid that I can't do any more.'

'Please don't bother to come out then.'

'No, I don't mean that. Peter will have to go into hospital.'

CHAPTER FOURTEEN

'You realise he may die.'

THE DOCTOR SOON arrived at our bungalow. Once he had examined Pete in his bedroom he rang the hospital and called the ambulance. The paramedics arrived, parking on the grass close to the porch. They put Pete in the recovery position before moving him. We were aghast at the turn of events. I think Pete was too ill to care as they moved him onto a stretcher. As the ambulance moved off it left great ruts in the damp ground. It was a constant reminder of that last time he left his home, until the grass grew again in the following summer.

On the adult medical ward Pete was given a side room and put on a drip to receive a high dose of antibiotics. Philip had returned from university the previous day and the three of us kept a vigil by Pete's bed. The junior doctors kept visiting him.

In the early evening Philip went off to meet his friends in the pub.

'You realise he may die.'

The words of the junior doctor later that evening cut across our naive faith in the medical profession to solve Peter's problems. Did he understand the words blurted out across the room?

'Can't he go into intensive care?'

Pete had to have every chance but the young man did not seem to think it was appropriate. I was worried that Pete might not be treated in the same way as another young man of his age: a mistrust originating from a conversation I had had when Pete was a baby about possible cardiac surgery. I was told that at that time there were then some doctors who would not carry out heart operations on babies with Down's syndrome, although this changed subsequently.

I reflect now how people with learning disabilities and their parents had to face the news during Covid that sometimes blanket Do Not Resuscitate Notices were used for people with learning disabilities. How did they react to the delays in responding to their requests for prioritisation for vaccinations? Organisations campaigned, individuals and families wrote letters to government and MPs to no avail. In the end it needed celebrities to get involved. Jo Whiley and Ian Rankin campaigned on behalf of their respective sister and son. Then there was a response. It makes me angry and sad that it took so long for their voices of people with learning disabilities to be heard. Perhaps I wasn't wrong to be wary those years ago.

That evening, the consultant on duty was suddenly at Peter's bedside. He looked at me.

'Do you want Peter to go into intensive care? He will have to go to another hospital. We have no beds.'

'Can we talk outside?'

I didn't want Pete to hear this conversation. I wasn't sure what was going on. We established that he would be moved. We needed to call Philip who was out with friends and we didn't know which pub he was in. We called the school where there was a staff party in the hopes that Philip's friend's dad might know his whereabouts. He, a Methodist minister, unused to pubs, went on a search, a new experience for him. Luckily, he soon found Philip and Tim. I shall never forget Philip sitting wretched by Pete's bed, his eyes full of tears.

The school chaplain appeared on the ward. He took Philip off to collect Tim so that he would have company as he spent the night at home. We were to accompany Pete. He was taken to the theatre to be sedated and prepared for his journey. Andy and I went to the relatives' room. A young anaesthetist came to talk to us about the dangers of what was being done and the risk of septicaemia. As far as I was concerned, Pete had to be restored to full health. He was going to a prestigious hospital and this might be an opportunity to solve his problems. How naïve I was.

In the middle of the night we set out, Pete in the ambulance and Andy and I in the car along the icy dual carriageway. When we arrived, we were not able to see him straight away and we were shown into another relatives' room. We could try to sleep in an armchair. A young woman was determined to recount to us how her boyfriend had fallen downstairs after a wedding. So began more than three months of hospital existence where we were drawn into the joys and tragedies of strangers. In hospital we seemed cut off from the mainstream of life, focused, like the other relatives we met, on the needs of our loved one.

I don't know that Pete would have remembered anything of those five days in intensive care in Cambridge surrounded by metal and glass. Everything seemed white or shiny grey, tubes and monitors everywhere, gowned figures always present. We sat beside him, talked to him, played his favourite tapes. Sometimes we were excluded as tests or treatments were carried out. We avoided the visitors' room. One family and their friends seemed to have taken it over. We preferred the concourse, where we could sit impersonally drinking a cup of coffee. Andy and I would go into the chapel and pray. I cannot remember what we prayed for: that everything would be all right I suppose. On the Sunday there was a carol service. We felt totally removed from Christmas festivities. We crept into the chapel after the service hoping to be quiet. The clergy were relaxing, joking in the vestry over their coffee. We left. We could not concentrate.

Did Pete notice the changed rhythms in hospital over the weekends, the feeling of everything being on hold? The bustle resumed on a Monday. He was to be given a scan and we were told to arrive in the afternoon. A young doctor called us into a small room. They had thought Pete might have a tumour or meningitis, but no, he had suffered a series of massive strokes to the brainstem. We might be involved in a decision to turn off his life support; it was possible that he was already technically dead. I broke down. He held my hand, this man, young enough to be my son, who had to convey such devastating news.

We went into Pete's room. He lay inert.

'There's always hope.'

These were the nurse's first words to us. Did Pete hear them? To us they sounded hollow, but we behaved as if they were true. We continued to talk to him and to play his favourite music. Now we find it hard if we hear *the Four Seasons*. Philip was our greatest support, encouraging, and practical. He sought to reassure us, visited the hospital regularly and appeared to be coping. I am sure it was at a cost to himself.

When I woke on the Tuesday morning, it was as if I was peering into a black abyss, a world without Pete. We had some post, a big card made by his friends at school. When we arrived at the hospital, we read out the names: Dawn, Charmeine, Tracy, Gary...

Briefly he opened his eyes.

'Well, I've been talking to him all morning with no response and you arrive and he looks at you,' his nurse remarked.

Could there be hope? There was no more talk of switching off life support systems.

'I think Pete will go back to our hospital soon.'

'No, you can't be right.'

I was aghast at Andy's words. I felt cocooned in the expertise of a large teaching hospital. Sure enough, the next day, we were told Pete would be moved in the afternoon. There was a space in the intensive care locally. Once again Pete travelled in an ambulance along the dual carriageway. The change in environment was staggering. Whereas the overwhelming impression of the first intensive care was intensely clinical, Pete was now in a large room decorated in pastel shades, dominated by a large Christmas tree.

Did Pete notice? He was still very ill.

CHAPTER FIFTEEN

'He was surrounded with cards and balloons and an eighteenth-birthday banner hung over his bed.'

HOW DID PETE perceive his new environment? He was shortsighted and did not hear well at the best of times. Perhaps he sensed a slightly more relaxed atmosphere? Was he aware we were there? We played his tapes quietly on the cassette recorder on the ledge behind his bed. His nurse regularly administered his medication and took readings.

On Christmas morning, Andy, Philip and I took in Pete's presents and opened them one by one. We kept talking to him.

'Look at this smart dressing gown.'

'What a lovely tee shirt.'

It seemed to be a year when most of the presents were clothes. I couldn't help but wonder whether Pete would ever wear them.

Andy and I had Christmas lunch in the staff dining room. It felt subdued. Philip, still in his vegetarian phase, went home. My mother was spending Christmas with my brother that year. Daily I would ring her, my heart heavy, finding it difficult to talk about Pete's condition as he lay so still, with a tracheostomy, tube fed, on a ventilator, with a catheter. Andy kept in contact with his parents. Most of the other enquiry calls were directed to friends at that stage.

The young anaesthetist, supposedly on leave over Christmas, came in. She gained our admiration for her dedication and honesty as she discussed Pete's condition and prognosis. There was concern about indications of the level of his brain function.

The consultant psychiatrist who had been looking after Pete dropped in on her way home from visiting her family. Margaret the manager from the unit kept in close touch as her husband was also in the hospital. Pete was surrounded by concern and love.

Then Pete was off the ventilator, just on oxygen. That was progress! We were warned that he would have to move back to the medical ward soon. Very late one evening, the phone rang,

'We are going to move Pete now. We need his bed.'

'I'll have to ring you back.'

I was too choked to speak. How could my son be wheeled down the dimly lit hospital corridors, late at night, not knowing where he was going? I expect that I overestimated his awareness but I was very upset. The next day we visited Pete on the ward where he had first been admitted less than a fortnight previously. It felt like a lifetime. He was in a six-bed bay for men near the desk. Initially he was by the window, but the oxygen supply behind the bed became faulty and he was moved to the bed in the centre on the opposite side.

The individual attention and steady pace of the intensive care was in great contrast to the hectic pace of life on the mixed medical ward. I so wished there had been a high dependency unit for a transition phase. We spent as much time as we could with Pete each day. We were impressed with the dedication of the staff but were aware they were over stretched. This was particularly the case in the evening when only two trained nurses were on duty and each had to have a supper break. Often we would stay beyond the end of visiting hours, until they had both returned to make sure we could oversee Pete's needs. Andy and I were taught how to use the suction machine and would draw the secretions off his chest through the tracheostomy tube. Some days it seemed in almost constant use. We would periodically moisten his lips with a sponge. Within a few days Pete had a gastrostomy, and a feeding tube was inserted in his stomach. How did he view this? He had so loved his food and mealtimes had been social events. I was assured that men in a similar situation who had enjoyed their steak and chips had communicated that it was not wholly negative.

Pete's eighteenth birthday was on January 11th. Fortunately, no one on the bay was desperately ill at that time and we were able to hold a party in the afternoon. We put cake and drinks by the window as it didn't seem fair to have them close to him. His head teacher and several staff came across from Ipswich bringing a card made by his friends. Suzanne played *Happy Birthday* on the guitar. Margaret and Gina came from the unit. His friend Daniel, who used to sit in with him, called in with his girlfriend. He was surrounded with cards and balloons and an eighteenth birthday banner hung over his bed. Pete seemed really alert that day, as if he had rallied for the occasion. He was becoming more aware and defying the early prognosis of one of the neurologists that he was in a persistent vegetative state. In the evening Andy and I went for a meal to a local pub, leaving the number with the hospital in the belief that we should celebrate the joy Pete had brought us over eighteen years.

The next day Pete seemed poorly and that was the pattern for the next few weeks. Some days were better than others. At times he became restless and arched his back, as if he was trying to scream. Because of his tracheostomy, no sounds could emerge. One day I could bear this no longer and left his bedside in tears. A friend who had dropped in to see him came and sat beside me. Several times we feared for his life. Once his tube became blocked and he went blue. Several times he had serious infections. The consultant involved us in discussions about his treatment and we agreed that he should be given antibiotics if he got an infection. We were brought into the grey world of medicine, deciding between various options. One night we sat up with him, as there was real concern about his condition. At four o'clock he suddenly looked alert and the crisis passed. Pete showed great tenacity and courage and we could only be there beside him.

Another concern was to improve his quality of life and to stimulate him. I mused ruefully that in his earliest years we had worked to find ways to facilitate his progress and now it was as if we were starting all over again. Pete's school staff were his main support and came over regularly. They provided a bag of objects of different textures that Pete could feel and left it with us. Eventually we made contact with the hospital education-service and the tutor also supported him in the final weeks on the ward. The physiotherapists worked with him once or twice a week, supporting him into a sitting position. They also gave us exercises to do with him and each day we would systematically move his arms and legs in the ways that we had been shown. Where his muscles had appeared withered, they began to strengthen. Pete was measured for a wheelchair and its arrival marked another milestone.

I felt possessed by a determination to do all that I could for Pete to improve his life. I now recall with some amazement that I asked for him to have new hearing aids. He had had a severe hearing loss diagnosed when he was nearly eight but within a year he had rejected the aids. I thought we could try again and enhance Pete's senses. Pete made it quite clear that he did not share my enthusiasm.

It was not all work and stimulation. Pete listened to his music through headphones which he had previously disliked. We also rented a television and he seemed to enjoy looking at the small screen over his bed. Most days a friend or two would visit. Some people found that they could not cope with seeing him so disabled. Others were a great support to him and to us. Pete's school also sent presents to encourage him and us. On Valentine's Day, Pete had an enormous red heart signed by all his friends hanging over his bed. One of his teachers gave up time some weekends to sit with Pete while Andy and I went for a walk. Another friend visited him on a Monday afternoon when I had classes to teach. Fortunately, the other classes were early in the morning before visitors were welcome on the ward.

We would take short breaks while Pete was turned or washed. and we became frequenters of the hospital cafeteria. Most days, I would slip into the chapel. It seemed important to have a little time to reflect. I could sit before the icon of Mary and Jesus, thinking about the bond of Mother and Son. We would keep in touch with Philip at university. How did his worries affect his studies? He never told the authorities about his situation. He came home for a university reading week to see his brother. One night after visiting Pete the three of us went together to the Indian restaurant Pete had so enjoyed. It seemed important to try to do ordinary things amid our extraordinary lives and to cherish our family memories. Could we look to the future and what kind of future would that now be?

CHAPTER SIXTEEN

'If the hospital was no longer the right place, where should Peter go?'

THE WEEKS WENT by. It was becoming increasingly clear that an acute medical ward was not the best place for Pete once he was stabilised. The winter months were taking their toll and the bay became full of seriously sick people. The first death when we were present occurred on a Sunday night. Curtains were drawn hurriedly round the bed next to Pete and the crash team summoned. I could not help but wonder how the atmosphere affected him. How did he feel when deaths occurred in the night? Was he aware of them? Was he frightened? There were more deaths than usual. We had offers of counselling, although we did not take them up. This was not available for Pete. We could only be there for him, supporting him with our love.

If the hospital was no longer the right place, where should Peter go? He needed twenty-four-hour nursing care. If he was nursed at home, he would have an agency nurse and a second person at times as two people were needed to turn him. He also needed a room with the space to accommodate a bed, hoist and large wheelchair, which needed a very big turning space. There was only one room of that size in our school bungalow: the lounge/dining room. We had put our house in Scarborough on the market as we might need to move out of the school accommodation if Pete was to be cared for at home. That would take time to organize.

Bungalows for people with learning disabilities run by the health authority (overshadowed by the deserted former long-stay hospital) and a room in a local nursing home were considered and rejected: the one because Pete needed such extensive care and the other because we thought it was not appropriate at his age. I rang a local home for younger disabled people. Again, they could not provide the nursing care.

'Have you heard of the recently opened Sue Ryder home for people of working age in Ipswich?'

I was on the phone there straightaway and arranged to visit with Andy the following weekend.

The Chantry was an eighteenth century house. Its façade was similar in its grey classicism and symmetry to that of Culford Hall, which had been so familiar to Pete. Both buildings were surrounded by extensive grounds with some magnificent cedar trees. The Chantry stood in the centre of a public park and so it felt as if it was linked to the community. The sister was full of enthusiasm for the life they supported people to lead there. The home had the added advantage of being ten minutes from Pete's school and he could keep in touch with some of his friends. The matron must have been very surprised to get my phone call at the beginning of the next week.

'I would like my son to come to your home. I am sure it is the right place for him.'

She was understandably cautious. The home was registered for people with physical disabilities. She would need to visit him. When she came to the hospital, she later told us that she wanted to take him straightaway to the Chantry to give him a new life.

We had to talk to the various agencies, particularly health and social services. A case conference was called. The local Mencap regional officer came to meet Peter and attended the meeting as an independent voice to support us all. It was agreed in principle that Peter could go to the Chantry. His prime needs were medical, his learning disability was secondary. The funding would be found. In the long run, with continued improvement, the aim would be for him to return home.

Louise, the junior sister, visited to find out about all Peter's needs. By Easter there would be a new beginning. Once more Pete would take the road to Ipswich and we would regularly drive down that route.

I remember the journey we made in the ambulance to the Chantry that spring day when Pete was moved. Jane, his named nurse from the hospital, was with us. The sister had had tears in her eyes as she said goodbye to Pete after his three-month stay on her ward. Jane and I talked quietly about the previous three months, about her plans to move to the States. We reassured Pete. Was he aware of the big changes occurring in his life?

'The stretcher won't go up in the lift.'

What was it like for Pete to arrive at an unfamiliar house, to be surrounded by strange faces and voices, to be hoisted chalk-faced, into the unfamiliar wheelchair and taken upstairs in the lift to his room, Tamarisk? I wonder if he ever noticed the view across the park. With his short sight, it is more likely that his immediate surroundings caught his attention, the chintz curtains, the pale blue walls, a sharp contrast with the starkness of the hospital.

I shall never forget our visit to Chantry on the day after his arrival. We were longing to see Pete, wondering how he had fared in the previous eighteen hours. We rushed up to his room, only to find it empty.

'Pete's in the dayroom.'

We hurried downstairs and found him sitting in a reclining chair, fully dressed, wearing the patterned blue shirt we had bought for his eighteenth birthday. It was as if he was celebrating after the months he had lain in the hospital, naked under the sheets.

The room was a hive of activity. Radio One was playing; Betty was busy making cards; Mike was looking suspiciously at Pete, a newcomer; John's head was resting on his arms; Donna was keeping an eye on everybody, encouraging, caring. I again wonder what Pete made of it all.

Those early weeks assumed a pattern. Each day, the nurses would hoist Pete into the shower tray or give him a bed-bath. He would be dressed and go downstairs. Often he needed to go back to his bed for a rest in the early afternoon. Sometimes he went into the first-floor lounge with its wonderful floor-to-ceiling bay window. Always the oxygen and the trolley with suction were beside him. Four times a day he needed a nebuliser to keep his airways moist. At 12.30, water was poured through the gastrostomy tube. I can never look at cranberry juice on the supermarket shelf without a jolt of recognition. At 2.30 it was given to him to help prevent urine infections. At 5 o'clock he was linked to his feed for the night. He always liked routine. Did he appreciate the pattern to his days?

At times during those early weeks he seemed very tired. We would drive over, anticipating our visit with pleasure, only to find Pete fast asleep. Sometimes he had sweaty attacks and needed paracetamol. His temperature control had been damaged by the strokes. Gradually through the summer, this seemed to improve. At last, the sides to his wheelchair were changed and properly adjusted. I did wonder also whether he had felt insecure and uncomfortable and whether this had contributed to his clamminess. Gradually Pete was weaned off the oxygen, although it always remained by his side to be used occasionally. It seemed as if there was progress.

'Peter smiled at me today.'

The nurses and care assistants became excited as he showed his pleasure. He grinned at us. We were full of joy and marvelled that after all his suffering and with his enormous disabilities, he could be happy. All we could offer was our love and our time.

It had been hard to hand over Pete's physical care to others after almost eighteen years. I know I scrutinised every action of the nurses to ensure that everything was right for him, until I learned gradually to relax. We were able to enjoy his company while others concentrated on his daily needs. In those early days, Louise seemed to spend hours on the phone, chasing all the pieces of equipment he required. We were glad we didn't have that distraction.

Easter fell just two weeks after Pete's move. Philip was home from university, and it was his twenty-first birthday on the Monday. My mother came down on the train from Scarborough to celebrate with us. She had a nasty cough that she could not throw off. We did not realise that she too was very ill. On Easter Sunday there was a service led by the chaplain, Revd. Peter Gibbs. Andy and I attended it. Pete sat in the lounge with his Gran, watching *Grease* on the television. Although he had seen the show, he was not particularly interested. Perhaps he wasn't close enough but he could hardly sit right by the screen obscuring the view for others as he might have done at home. Several of Peter Gibbs' parishioners came upstairs to talk to the residents, who had not been able to go to the chapel. I felt frustrated that they could only see Pete as he was then and did not know the young man that he had been. It was as if they only saw one aspect.

On the Monday, we asked if Pete could be in his room for our visit. Pete sat in the reclining chair supported by pillows. He preferred this to his wheelchair. Andy, my mother, Philip and I sat and talked to Pete and listened to his music. It felt like the old days. It had been inhibiting to sit in the lounge and to know that the whole room could hear our conversation. It became the norm for us to visit Pete in Tamarisk. It became our little world.

CHAPTER SEVENTEEN

'The Jungle Book .... made him chuckle to himself when the elephant didn't forget.'

WE LIKE TO think that Pete appreciated that we tried to make the room homely with familiar objects surrounding him. We bought a television, video and music centres. We took over a chest of drawers and some shelves were put up. We arranged Pete's possessions, his christening tankard, the wooden interlocking letters of his name, the carved tiny wooden guitar, and photos of the family and his friends. I would bring in flowers and arrange them in a vase. Pete would look at his father as much as to say, 'What's she doing now?' I often thought of his expression when I put flowers on his grave.

We hung some pictures. Philip's A-level painting of an enormous deep pink bloom dominated one wall. Marion, his teacher, brought him a picture of a brightly coloured cockerel. I put up the view of two small figures sitting on a seat overlooking the North Bay in Scarborough, painted by my mother. I told Pete they represented him and his small cousin, Suzie. I am not sure he believed me but he seemed to like the idea. Every time I saw mobiles I speculated as to whether they would have been good additions to the couple in his room. Andy and I would visit individually or together most days, usually in the afternoons, fitting round the requirements of our jobs and the home's activities. We would look at photos, play music, watch videos, talk, read stories. It was as if our real life was there.

Amazingly, Pete seemed to be making progress in some areas, doing things he'd not done before. He would now follow a story. We would read him the Ladybird version of *The Railway Children* or watch *The Lion King* or *The Jungle Book* which made him chuckle to himself when the elephant didn't forget. We would play a greater range of music than he tolerated before, although his favourites still predominated. We assured the staff that he preferred Enya or classical music to the local radio station. Despite his enormous disabilities, he communicated through his eyes and expression. We all loved it when his face was illuminated by his smile.

In the first weeks, Pete would go to the activity room and also have regular physiotherapy, which was not his favourite option and apparently he did not cooperate that willingly. Twice a week in term time, staff from Pete's school would work with him. In August an occupational therapist was appointed. She devoted much of her energy to those with the severest disabilities. A snoezelen corner was established. We too learnt to use the hoist so that we could move Pete from and into his wheelchair and then at weekends we could take him there, enabling him to relax on the mats and look at the lights and mirrors.

Pete really preferred his reclining chair to his wheelchair. In that very hot summer, he appreciated relaxing in his room, a fan on his face. The wheelchair was considered better for his posture. It did also enable us to take him out into the public park. We would wheel him by the bowling green and around the pond, sometimes as far as the cricket pitch. On one memorable day, a cricketer came over to us.

'It's Pete, isn't it?'

He had taught Pete in the Lower school at Belstead.

On another occasion when Philip was back home, we were walking with Pete in the park. His brother thought he should have more excitement in his life. We walked a short distance along the busy London Road and Philip went ahead of us, pushing Pete fast in his wheelchair down the hill back to the house. One weekend the staff played rounders in the park and Pete seemed to think that was very amusing. On another a steel band played in the courtyard. We anticipated that he would love that, but he sweated profusely and clearly felt unwell. He had to return to his room.

Originally it had been intended that Pete should be in one of the big rooms as John wanted to share, and past experience suggested that Pete would prefer a companion. On his arrival he had a bowel infection which necessitated him being on his own. It took a long time to clear and another new resident moved in with John. By that stage it was obvious that Pete had settled on his own with his many visitors. Sometimes he would be wheeled into Will and Simon's room, and I think he enjoyed spending time with the younger residents.

He had particular friends among the staff. Carmel along with Louise was his named nurse. Carmel would try to get him to sign 'yes' by raising his thumb and would joke and make him laugh. He was greatly loved because he accepted the care he received with dignity and grace. One staff nurse described him as an angel, which is certainly not a word I would have used before his illness. It was as if his frustrations had left him and he was at peace with himself. It makes me sad when I read that people think that the life of those with profound disabilities is not worth living. It was lovely to read *The Diving Bell and the Butterfly*. Jean Dominique Bauby was able to dictate it by moving his eyelid, following severe strokes. Nowhere did he say he wanted to die. He lived in the present and took pleasure from the company of his young daughter.

It amuses me as I think of a phone call I received from parliament some years later when I was working. I had been interviewed by the Scrutiny Committee for the Mental Incapacity Bill as it was initially called. The parliamentary officer wanted to check that I had really said so many 'verys' in one of my responses. He asked if the stenographers had made a mistake. In my concern about how decisions might be made about treatment for someone who was incapacitated I told them 'I think there is a danger that we are thinking about dying rather than about living ... and ... safeguards have to be very, very, very, very tough.' I assured him that I had meant to say 'very' four times! I was so glad that there was such a focus at the Chantry of enabling people to live as full a life as possible.

CHAPTER EIGHTEEN

'We shared the aim of the staff and his friends to make his life....as rich as possible.'

PETER'S LIFE CONTINUED to be varied. Marion, one of his teachers, was a great friend to him. She supported him by twice weekly visits in the autumn term. One week she took him into the park to look for leaves as they turned colour. The next week, she helped him varnish them and mount them on orange and green card. We had these framed in light ash. He was always pleased to see Marion.

One of his fellow students, Gary, visited him in the Chantry. I remember Gary very well. When we visited the school after Pete had died, he showed me his carpentry.

'I like the patterns in the wood,' he said as he stroked the surface.

He was shocked to see his friend incapacitated. Did Pete sense that? Nonetheless we were wondering whether Pete would be able to get used to going out in the new minibus and whether he would eventually be able to visit his friends in school. In the event he had just one outing to Felixstowe with Louise. It took a lot of planning. Once again, he would have seen the familiar promenade.

We were looking ahead to a time when he might be stronger and able to visit us in the minibus. Having sold our own house in Scarborough in the June, we were trying to find a house close to the Chantry with the right accommodation. Sometimes on our way to and from Ipswich, we would make a diversion to view a house or bungalow. Nothing seemed suitable. It made us realise how difficult it is to find a home for someone with a large wheelchair. There were many obstacles: a step in the wrong place, insufficient turning space, rooms too small for the hoist and other equipment.

Although we were looking ahead to the times when Pete might be able to move beyond the close confines of the home, we shared the aims of the staff and his friends to make his life there as rich as possible. Did he appreciate the variety? One day there was a choral concert. He was one of the most enthusiastic members of the audience, smiling broadly. His friend, Margaret, who used to play the piano for him regularly when he was younger, introduced us to a family of very musical young people. They gave Pete a chamber concert of his own in the Long Room. As the melodies became livelier, he grinned from ear to ear. A friend from church would bring along her violin and play solos for him in his room. Other friends visited.

He continued to be part of the church. We needed to think about Pete's confirmation. In the past he had indicated he was puzzled that he wasn't offered communion, looking up enquiringly at his vicar, Richard, as he received a blessing. Before his illness we had planned that his confirmation would happen in the March. I had been trying to find materials for his preparation but had only been able to find two booklets, one for people who could not read from the Church Army, and the other for people with learning disabilities seeking membership of the Baptist Church. Each was well illustrated.

Everything had been put on hold. On the Sunday that had previously been planned for his confirmation, while Pete was still in hospital, the Bishop of Dunwich, the Rt Revd. Jonathan Bailey, came with Richard and visited Pete on the ward. Pete amazed us by responding to this stranger by raising his arm to him. We arranged to get in touch when Pete had settled in the

Chantry to set a date for the service that could be held in the chapel there.

Richard came over to Ipswich to transfer Pete's pastoral care to Peter Gibbs, the chaplain. I looked out the meagre material I had been able to assemble. Andy and Peter held four confirmation classes for our Pete, focusing on God the Father, Jesus, confirmation and communion. He seemed very absorbed. When the chaplain told him that God was like his Dad, he looked across at Andy and grinned. Andy made a scrapbook and would talk to Pete about the pictures of the Creation, Jesus' life and the Church.

We fixed the confirmation date for late August. More than thirty people gathered in the chapel: staff and residents, members of our local church, Pete's friends and our friends. My mother, very ill with cancer at this stage, invited a friend to visit her at her home at the time of the service and they read it together, sharing in the moment from a distance of over two-hundred miles. Pete reclined in a chair by the table. We sang some of his favourite hymns, *Amazing Grace* and *Make me a Channel of your Peace.* At the point of the confirmation, Pete seemed to respond. Everyone shared communion. Since Pete couldn't swallow, the Bishop moistened his lips with the wine using his baptism spoon.

Afterwards we all gathered in the Long Room for a buffet lunch. Pete again was in a reclining chair. People greeted him. I can picture Wendy and her mother Sandra spending a long time with him. I also can see Suzie, his little cousin, nearly two years old, crouched down beside him, fascinated. My brother and his wife had come across from Somerset. The only other time Pete had seen Suzie was when she was a small baby. She had visited us in Scarborough. We had told him he must be very gentle and he had sat on the floor beside me looking across the room in great interest as she lay in her bouncing chair.

As the visitors dispersed in the early afternoon, Pete was taken upstairs to rest on his bed. He fell asleep straightaway. Many people told us they found the confirmation service very moving. For Richard and Bishop Jonathan, it was one of the highlights of their ministries. For Peter Gibbs 'it underlines the accessibility of the gospel to all people'.[8] To me it felt as if it was a step on Pete's spiritual journey and in that respect his experience was no different from that of others who came to a point when they made a public statement that they wished to belong to the Church.

Although we could count on the fingers of one hand the days when Pete had no one from outside the home visiting him, there were times when I couldn't see Pete. In August Andy and I took a week's holiday in Derbyshire to gather our resources. From May, I was making regular visits to see my mother in Scarborough to coincide with her cancer treatment. We supported her as she made a supreme effort to attend our niece, Suzie's christening in the south-west in September, as she was her latest grandchild. She amazingly felt well that weekend. In late October, I was called north and arrived in time to be with her through her last night and stayed to arrange the funeral. She was one of Pete's greatest friends and I was glad for her sake she died first.

We didn't know how long Pete would live. We hoped it would be years but we knew he was always susceptible to infection. He appeared stronger and stable. A speech therapist had shown us how to put his favourite cream cheese on his lips to encourage him to move his mouth. We were in discussions with the hospital about reversing the tracheostomy in the next few months, perhaps in the spring. One day, Pete put one foot over the other.

'Well done,' we cried.

8 Update, St Matthew's Church September/October 1995

The home experimented to see if he could do without his catheter but he failed to empty his bladder properly and it had to be replaced. Some weeks later it caused him problems and a second try to remove it seemed to be successful.

As the winter approached, I wondered whether there would be times when we would find it more difficult to get across to Ipswich. Peter Gibbs introduced us to Clare, a young mother living nearby, who came to see Pete and said she would like to visit regularly. One day stands out in my memory; I think it must have been in November. I travelled across in the morning and participated in the snoezelen session. Then Clare came and we took Pete for a walk as part of the process of her getting to know him. He seemed to welcome new friends and was at ease. In the afternoon Pete and I settled in his room to listen to his music and watch his videos. Six or seven hours flashed by.

In late November, Andy had a Saturday off and we decided to take up a friend's offer to stay in their Norfolk house for a Friday and Saturday night. We would visit Pete on our return on the Sunday, meeting up with Philip who had several days' leave from the group home for people with learning disabilities in London where, since completing his degree, he had been working from late September. He would then be with us for an early celebration of Andy's fiftieth birthday. Had we known what was going to happen, we would not have gone away, but we could take comfort that in his last days, Pete also saw his brother and his friends.

While we were away Pete had visits from Margaret and John, his Link family whom he had regularly visited in the past. Margaret recalled how he pleaded with his eyes for them to stay longer. On the Saturday, Tim who had sat in with him in our home for several years, also as part of the Suffolk Link scheme, took his children to see Pete.

'They liked Pete. He was a happy boy.'

On the Sunday we arrived in the afternoon in time to attend a service with the new bishop. We left Philip upstairs with Pete.

'We don't want to go to a boring old service do we, Pete?'

Pete grinned.

On the Monday Philip and I went across. I was trying to make plans with the staff for Pete to visit his school. Philip was talking to him. When it was time to leave, I kissed him and said,

'Dad's coming tomorrow and I'll see you Wednesday.'

He seemed happy although more sleepy than usual. Philip went back to London the next day and Andy returned from his visit on the Tuesday with reports that he had been content.

I used to have nightmares where the phone rings in the middle of the night. Unusually we had left the answerphone on. At about two o'clock the phone went. There was no message and believing Pete to be stable, my first thought was that it was a wrong number. It went again and then again. This time Andy answered. It was a call from the night staff at the Chantry. He returned to our bed.

'It's Pete. He's died.'

We were shocked. Although we knew he was vulnerable, it seemed out of the blue. Our immediate reaction was to wish to go across to Ipswich. Andy however had been told that, because it was a sudden death, a policeman was outside Pete's room. We would be able to see him in due course. We lay waiting for morning. There was a hollow and an emptiness in the centre of our beings, a pain too deep for tears.

CHAPTER NINETEEN

'Peter gave something to us all. I know he filled me with a feeling of warmth and wonder.'

DURING THE FOLLOWING week we had to do all the tasks that death requires. We collected Pete's belongings from the Chantry. It was strange to walk into an unusually subdued atmosphere in the home. We entered Tamarisk. Despite the empty bed, as we moved Peter's possessions it was as if he was lingering there with us. We couldn't explain why we didn't feel bereft but strangely and temporarily comforted.

In the old Ipswich registry office, where we went to register Peter's death - he had developed septicaemia - the harshness of reality hit us. It seemed incongruous that we were even within hearing distance, let alone close to those recording the other momentous moments of life: birth and marriage. I reflected that Pete's great-great grandfather's marriage had been recorded some 150 years previously in a registry office in Ipswich. Who could have predicted, with the mobility of families, that this might have been the case?

A couple of days later, we visited Pete at the undertakers and gently kissed him goodbye.

We spent hours preparing for a funeral. Ironically it would take place on the day we had planned to have his monthly communion service. I had found the services we shared with Pete in his room, since his confirmation, particularly meaningful. As Peter Gibbs prepared the bread and wine, Pete's face would light up. In the November, we prayed for wholeness. I never dreamed that the next planned date, December 7th would be the day of his funeral.

We planned that it should be a celebration of Peter's life. Margaret, whose music he loved, played the organ. We walked the few yards across the grass to the nearby church. As we entered, we could see it was full and we felt sustained by the joy of the music Pete had so loved. '*Give me joy in my heart, keep me praising...*' We felt surrounded by the love of those present. The service started with the *Easter Hymn* from *Cavalleria Rusticana*. I looked across at the three floral tributes. Ours was intentionally simple, the one from the Home was a floral cushion with a treble clef acknowledging Pete's love of music, and the third was from Pete's school friends who had each placed a carnation in a basket. That nearly broke me.

Richard, as Pete's former pastor, and Peter Gibbs, as his present one, shared the service which included them reading our own memories as we didn't trust ourselves to be able to speak in public. We concluded with the words of a poem written by a member of staff from Belstead.

'So much has been said, yet no words have been spoken.

So much has been given, yet no presents open.'

Pete's godfather, Revd. Trevor Shannon, did a reading. The committal prayer dwelt on the thread of life which we were reminded had been so fragile for Pete for almost a year.

As we left the church and walked down the snow-covered path, we heard the triumphant music of Purcell's *Trumpet Voluntary*.

We surrounded the grave and Andy, Philip and I each cast a white carnation onto the coffin. We walked away from the graveyard and back to our bungalow where family and friends would join us. Our living room was crammed after the service. I would never have imagined that I could have coped with this without breaking down, but I was glad for Pete's friends from Ipswich to see his home.

‘Pete used to have his video over there,’ I told his teachers, wanting them to imagine how it had been.

‘It’s a lovely setting here,’ said one as she looked out across the grass to the whitened trees.

‘Yes, though I think Pete might have liked a busy road outside to watch. It was lovely in the summer. We had lots of barbecues.’

Gradually people made their farewells. We then started on the hard path of finding meaning to our lives as we no longer had the task of sustaining Pete, who had enriched our family for nearly nineteen years. Somehow, we had to learn to live with grief and loss and to retain all that he taught us about living life in his own way, communicating without words, valuing friends and love. Philip later observed that the three of us had been like a triangle with Pete in the middle. We had to find a new way of being as a family. Amid the pain, we could take pleasure in the way he touched so many lives. Our neighbour, Gordon Langley wrote

‘Wasn’t it wonderful that a young lad could fill the church and having to find extra chairs? The Vicar was right: Peter gave something to us all. I know he filled me with a feeling of warmth and wonder.’

POSTSCRIPT

YES PETE, YOU continue to have an enormous impact on our lives. You helped to determine Philip's choice of work, initially with people with learning disabilities and later in mental health. You know, one day his daughter, Autumn, when she was quite small said to me, 'I wish I'd known Uncle Pete.' I was pleased Philip had talked to her about you. You would have loved her. I can imagine how you would have led her to the piano or found her violin for her to play. You would have loved Kerry, Philip's partner too. They are a family with a strong sense of social justice which Philip says you gave to him.

Your Dad holds you deep in his heart. You were always his greatest friend. The only time I can remember him really cross with you was when you tried to pinch food off his plate! In recent years, the five of us have had a meal together on your birthday, remembering how you loved celebration meals.

I am sure you influenced Fiona and Anna, your friends from Durham, in their choice of careers, the one teaching children with special needs and the other a clinical psychologist. You certainly determined my own next steps in work, leaving history teaching, joining the Mental Health Foundation and helping to set up the Foundation for People with Learning Disabilities within it. It all felt like something I had to do, like a compulsion.

One of the key lessons I learnt from you was that people with learning disabilities who do not use words, can and should be heard. I know that sometimes we did not understand you but we tried to listen to what you were telling us through your expressions and gestures. You could sign 'please' in Makaton and thought that should open all sorts of doors. When we didn't get what you were saying without words it caused you frustration, but we always tried to discover your wishes and you certainly conveyed how you felt.

Some of our early projects at the Foundation focused on enabling those who do not use words to make choices and have influence over their lives. We called this the Choice Initiative. I think of Alan (not his real name) who was supported to find work experience he would enjoy. He had shown that he liked to be surrounded by people and by noises such as the telephone ringing, the radio playing. He had a placement in a Toy Library which suited him well. He indicated that he was fascinated by the photocopier and its sounds. Working on that became a favourite task. The manager said, 'He is missed the weeks he isn't here.'[9]

You know, Pete, it was a big change when you were born. I became what they call a family carer, continuing to teach history part-time and putting a career on hold. Then I had another transition, this time becoming a professional mixing with other professionals, researchers, senior civil servants and politicians! It was a good time because soon the government was wanting to focus on meeting the needs of people with learning disabilities. We launched our report and video from what we had learnt from the Choice Initiative where people like Alan could communicate what they would like to do. A senior civil servant attended. She was developing a policy document, *Valuing People*. I was so happy to read subsequently 'People with learning disabilities currently have little control over their own lives, though almost all, including the most severely disabled,

9 Foundation for People with Learning Disabilities *Everyday Lives, Everyday Choices* (Foundation for People with Learning Disabilities 2000)

are capable of making choices and expressing their views and preferences'.[10]

You showed us the centrality of friendship and that was also important in our projects at the Foundation. We looked at what people with learning disabilities told us was important in their lives and friendship was very high on the list. It was heart rending to read about one young man who had never had a friend and been lonely all his life.[11] He, like you, would certainly have enjoyed some of the activities of the Friendship Club, part of People First Dorset.

Some people in our research said being part of a faith community was important to them but they did not always have that opportunity.[12] I think that you valued being a member of the church. I remember you as a little boy making your happy noises as we explored the ruins of Mount Grace Priory in Yorkshire and stood in the former chapel. Did you have a sense of a holy space?

Do you know, Pete, I think we were in so many ways fortunate in the support you and we received? You had so many good teachers and teaching assistants. You could go and stay at Eston House with Sister Mac, at the Family Help Unit and with Margaret and John from the Link scheme. We had support to plan for your future before you became ill.

In your lifetime there were big steps to end segregation and to provide support in the community. Policies continued to

---

10 Department of Health *Valuing People: A new strategy for learning disability for the 21st century* 44 (Department of Health 2001)

11 Swinton, J. and Powrie E. *Why Are We Here? Meeting the spiritual needs of people with learning disabilities* London: (Mental Health Foundation 2004)

12 Hatton ,C. et al.(2005) *Religious Expression, A Fundamental Human Right: The report of an action research project on meeting the religious needs of people with learning disabilities* Available from https://www.learningdisabilities.org.uk/learning-disabilities/publications/religious-expression-fundamental-human-right

improve for many people with learning disabilities This lasted for a few years. Then sadly, because of austerity some services were cut restricting opportunities and then the Covid epidemic arrived. People with learning disabilities and their families were particularly vulnerable and they became more isolated as supports were withdrawn.

Your story is a plea to all of us to challenge discrimination, to act imaginatively and enable all people with learning disabilities to be treated equally and to lead full and healthy lives in their own communities. Recently, as I was looking through my books and papers I read, 'I know that when I look back in old age that I will count the eighteen years spent with Peter among the richest of my life as we shared the enjoyment of celebrations, outings, picnics, friendships, and, above all, music... we shared love, sadness and happiness.'[13]

Pete, you taught us so much.

13 Morgan, H. 2004 'Thoughts on Suffering: A parent's view' *Journal of Religion Disability and Health* 8 3/4 pp 107-119

About the Author

IN HER FIRST book, *Through Peter's Eyes*, Hazel Morgan captured the life of her younger son, who had Down's syndrome, up to the age of eleven, first in Durham and then in Suffolk. Now in her second memoir *The Joy of Knowing Pete: Much was said, yet no words spoken* she focuses on what Peter taught her in his teenage years and how he touched the lives of so many people. Peter's death shortly before his nineteenth birthday prompted her to change career. She had studied Modern History at St Hugh's College Oxford and taught for many years in secondary, further and higher education. Subsequently she became a Co-Director of the Foundation for People with Learning Disabilities, then part of the Mental Health Foundation. Now in retirement she is a trustee of People First Dorset. She lives in Dorset with her husband and enjoys being close to her son, Philip, and his family, reading novels, researching family history and exploring the local area.

About this book

'This is a beautiful and moving memoir - of joy, grief, pain, faith, belonging, love, and a life well lived.'

Chris Hatton Professor of Social Care Manchester Metropolitan University

'Through a series of snapshot recollections and the words of those who knew him, Hazel Morgan provides the reader with a memorable and poignant account of her son's life. Pete was born with profound learning disabilities and the book follows his life during his teenage years spent at the family's tied bungalow in the grounds of the school where his father was deputy head. The kindness and love of those surrounding Pete shines through, with the family, and those that know Pete, frequently finding ingenious ways to adapt to his complex needs. They are repaid by Pete's ability to communicate despite having no language. The joy that Pete expresses in his own particular way radiates throughout the book and leaves the reader with the sense that this young man's life touched a great many others.'

Virginia Astley Writer

'Through the eyes of a mother this book touches your heart and the words of a mother filled with pride for her son Peter, whose life was too short, touch your soul. It is a beautiful book with so many memories of joy, love and sadness for the loss of a son. The words must be read and resonate to those that may forget that the people they see as part of their work is someone's son, brother, friend and deserves a life filled with joy and love.

This book is beautifully written with fairness and equality at the heart, reminding us that all life is precious.'

Christine- Koulla Burke Director the Foundation for People with Learning Disabilities

'Hazel's book is a moving account of how one family learned to live - often joyfully - alongside a young son with a disability. There is not a shred of self pity here, only a reminder of the brevity of all our lives and our universal desire to make meaning.'

Sally Bayley Writer

'Hazel's memoir creates a strong sense of a mother's connection with a son who needed huge amounts of daily support to live life well. She takes us on a journey with Pete, through his teenage years until his untimely death. That journey includes his father, Andy, and brother Philip and quietly creates a picture of how they all adapted their way of doing things so that Pete felt safe, whilst also exploring his own loves and interests. There is plenty of gentle humour around the way Pete expresses his choices and directs the family, without using words, often with the aim of ending up in a café to enjoy something to eat.

The memoir is full of other people who Pete drew into their lives, reflecting the importance of friendship and connections for people with learning disabilities. It also has a strong sense of place as they travel around to visit people, or for holidays, and Pete finds ways to engage with different environments. Interwoven with these stories are Hazel's concerns for her son's future and the broader issues of changing policy and practice that impact on the lives of people with learning disabilities. This memoir is a wonderful insight into how the family around someone with profound disabilities are at the core of someone having, in the words of Hazel and Andy, 'a complete life' but also subtly hints at the need for the rest of society to be more inclusive and for a greater national policy commitment to people with learning disabilities.'

Christine Towers Director Together Matters

Printed in Great Britain
by Amazon

81891057R00068